PRAISE FOR
Over Bridg

"A well written, delightful, endearing and moving book. The voice, which first draws one in and then lingers in the mind of the readers, is the voice of a bright and tender heart."

—Dr. Maria B. Oparnica Simić

"Falcone's memoir is a Venetian experience where family, food, love and everyday humor populate every page. Wonderfully Italian and completely universal, it's a must read for Italy lovers everywhere."

—The Florentine
Tuscany's English-speaking Newspaper

"Vignettes of life on the small island of Murano evoking larger-than-life characters and a simpler time that has slipped away forever."

—Chico Enterprise, Dan Barnett

"A keepsake of memories and a wealth of traditions, this book invites the readers to pull up a chair and be a part of the family. Touching and humorous, it's an alternative travel guide for those who want a real window on Venetian life."

—Linda Falcone, Author of *Italians Dance and I'm a Wallflower*

"This colorful and picturesque book could have been painted .. Because love of so many people wraps itself around the text, it becomes luminous."

—Teresa Bayol, author of *Panting after Chopin*

"An unforgettable book ... The enchanting setting of Murano and Venice, with their timeless beauty, and the richness of the traditions and values of family is reassuring and satisfying."

—Patricia L. McCreery

Over Bridges Across Tables

Lucia Barbini Falcone

TRAFFORD
PUBLISHING

Notes for Librarians: A cataloguing record for this book is available from
Library and Archives Canada at www.collectionscanada.ca/amicus/index-
e.html

ISBN 1-4120-6532-1

Barbini Falcone, Lucia
Over Bridges Across Tables: Growing up on the Island of Murano / by
Lucia Barbini Falcone.
Falcone Books / Published by arrangement with Trafford and with
McNaughton & Gunn, Inc.

For information:
Email Address: Orders@falconebooks.com
Website: http://www.falconebooks.com

1st printing, November 2005
2nd printing, October 2006
Printed simultaneously in the United States and Canada

Cover design by Sebastiano Padoan
Photo courtesy of Giuseppe Biscontin

*For my father and mother
who taught me how to build memories and to have
dreams*

What a wonder. . .What a miracle life is!
Nicolò Barbini

Acknowledgments

To my mother and father who taught me how to build my own memories; to my Italian and American families for the wonderful times we have spent together; to Malvina, who loves me; to my husband, Robert, who gives me strength; to my three daughters, Nicole, Chiara and Linda, who always support me and all of my endeavors; to my favorite son-in-law, Sebastiano Padoan, who designed the book cover; to Bill and Joyce Anderson, who believe in me; to the many wonderful teachers I've met along the way; to my friends, Térèse Bayol and Sophie Souroujon who helped and inspired me; to all of my dear friends who have touched my life in a very special way. . . I give my heartfelt thanks.

Contents

Author's Note

A few years ago, during one of my visits to Murano, I found that my mother had physically changed into someone I did not recognize anymore. For months, upon my return to the US, I could not shake my feelings of sadness, as I struggled with the realization that Mama would never again be the same.

Writing stories about my childhood helped me accept Mama's life-changing experience, as I realized that I had within me one important gift my father and mother gave my siblings and me: our wonderful memories, which are the threads that bind all of our lives together in a very special way.

I've written my stories as I see them now through the veil of time, using my creativity to add the details I didn't remember clearly. I've taken the liberty of rearranging names, and certain events out of respect for my family and friends in Murano, but the essence of the stories is true.

May your walk through Murano kindle some of your own memories, and may the scent of those memories linger on to give you much pleasure.

Prelude

Thunder and lightning strike with force against the red brick rooftop of my mama's house. I jump out of bed and run to close the windows so the incessant torrential rain does not enter.

We are alone in the house.

My sister Margherita and her family, who occupy the downstairs lower floor flat, are on vacation in the Dolomite Mountains and so is Gelmina, Mama's helper of more than fifty years and an honorary member of our family. My youngest sister, Giuliana, and her husband are on vacation as well. My oldest brother, Antonio, his wife and their eight children, and my brother, Pietro, his wife and their nine children, who live a five-minute walk from Mama's, are at the Lido Beach. My oldest sister, Gabri, who lives with Mama, is working nights as a nurse at the hospital in Venice.

I hurry into Mama's room to see if the summer thunderstorm has frightened her.

Mama is awake. Her body lies immobile like a dead weight under the white sheets and when I ask her if she is afraid, she looks at me like a defenseless child and says with sadness, "*Sì*," as she nods her head.

She looks so frail! Not like the Mama I remember. Not like the determined and energetic person she had been. No. All traces of Mama have disappeared. What lies in bed now is only an imitation of my mama, a forgery.

I sit by her bedside and look into her eyes. Eyes that tell me she knows she is not the same. Eyes that hide her humiliation, her *vergogna*. Eyes that know I know she has changed into someone even she, herself, does not recognize.

I hold her hand and stroke her short white hair back from her forehead. I caress her face. I reassure her that everything is going to be fine.

The boisterous thunder continues to roar all around us.

She nods and then whispers, "Is your baby well? Is he scared, too? Has he eaten his *minestrina*?"

I feel a tremendous sadness in my heart. I answer her as best I can that the baby is in America now, that he is beautiful and that, yes, in all probability he is eating his *minestrina* right at this moment.

I do not want to tell her that my "baby" girls are thirty-two, thirty and twenty-nine, and that the baby boy she is talking about is my six-month-old grandchild who has come to Italy this summer to be baptized in the same church where his parents and grandparents had been married.

"Take good care of him," she says. Then she smiles, satisfied to have contributed to the conversation.

Lightning strikes close by and illuminates the whole room for a few seconds. I see Mama looking at Papa's small portrait on her dresser. We both feel a strong connection to the smile Papa wore during his lifetime, forever imprinted in this old picture.

I wait a while longer. I stroke her head, her hand. I want to hold her, to cradle her on my knees, just like she did with us when we needed reassurance, way past our teenage years. I kiss Mama on the cheek and walk towards the kitchen amidst an aura of surrealism—the continuous sound of thunder accompanied by flashes of lightning and rain. I do not want to go to bed. I stop by the window and stare at the tenacious rain. I marvel at the power of nature, at the strength of its force, and think of the inner strength Mama and Papa displayed throughout their lives.

I walk around the kitchen table and sit in Papa's favorite chair, the place where Papa felt like a king—without a castle and material riches. I glance at the picture of our whole family on the wall. A younger Papa and Mama and we children sit around an elegant kitchen table that Mama and Gelmina prepared with care each day just as if we were expecting company. The kitchen table was the very place where Papa made a ritual of our daily repast, even when there was very little to eat.

I think of my heritage, of my childhood, of all of our relatives and friends who still live on the small island of Murano and in my mind I see a young girl walking over bridges with her siblings and friends, talking to relatives and passersby. Running amidst all of the familiar faces through the crowded *fondamenta, calle, campielli,* bridges on the island of Murano—a speck of land in the Venetian Lagoon adjacent to Venice where anyone who came from the outside, even if his provenance was from Venice, was considered a foreigner.

A place—which at times seems to appear and disappear within the depth of its capricious tides—not only linked by its bridges, but as well by the written and unwritten laws engraved within its social fabric.

My thoughts are interrupted by a sudden silence. I get up from Papa's chair and walk towards Mama's bedroom. She is asleep. The thunder and lightning have stopped. The rain has subsided. I glance out of the window. The earth is still. I return to my bed, but I cannot sleep.

Everything has changed; I think with sadness. I close my eyes and see the man I met on the *fondamenta* a few days before.

A man, an Italian tourist, stops me and asks, "Where is everybody? Where has everyone gone?" He laughs, and I join him.

"The vendors have gone home," I answer. "Everyone closes their shop around six."

Ready for an explanation, he looks at me with anticipation as if he were planning to discover some closely-guarded secret from our brief exchange. As if he wanted an explanation of why, at six o'clock, Murano resembles more of a ghost island than the vibrant community it once was.

The tourist throws his arms in the air, palms open towards me, and says, "Not even a cafè open to get an *aranciata*? It looks like a deserted island!"

We laugh again, and I say, "I think the cafés are closed on Wednesdays. It never used to be like this before. Things have changed in the last few years."

"*Va bene,*" he says, "we'll go back to Venice." Resigned, he shrugs his shoulders.

He crosses the bridge, *Ponte di Mezzo,* to join his two young sons who are already walking towards the lighthouse that looms in the distance. They stop from time to time to admire the pretty glass objects on display in the shop windows. I watch them walking through *Viale Garibaldi* till they disappear inside the boat station.

I turn around, anxious to recapture and to relive even a faint ray of my childhood memories, but I realize that this minute island, seemingly untouched by time, and the lifestyle of its people have changed—changed just like my eighty-eight year old Mama. My family, friends, neighbors, acquaintances and even people who provided me and my five siblings with a great sense of security and belonging, have disappeared, perhaps concealed behind the hustle and bustle of modernity.

I hold my gaze on the small shops that fold one onto the other along Murano's main artery. I observe the dark shop windows, which, over the years, like a Proteus, have metamorphosed into one big show room decked with a myriad of colorful, delicate glass objects.

I glance to the left, then right to embrace the parallel, two-story buildings that outline, on each side of the canal, the two fondamenta. Fragments of plaster are missing on the facades of the buildings. Sandy granules swirl and dive in the canal's water. Transported by the wind, they take refuge in the open entrances of the apartment buildings and factories. Geometric patches of red bricks nicked by too much wind, rain, fog, and humidity are a permanent distinction. It is all part of the charm of this island that consists of the laws of preservation, designed to maintain Murano's aesthetics intact, that give one the romantic illusion of an unaltered past.

In spite of such laws, in spite of its intact aesthetic appearance, in spite of the incessant effort to still bask in the glory of our ancestors and to pine for time long gone, life on the island has indeed changed. The limited boundaries of a bygone era, even within the confines of the small island, have vanished forever.

As I lie in bed, hoping to capture that part of Murano that is embedded within my soul, I glimpse a part of my life that I took with me thirty-four years ago when I came to America. I realize how fortunate I have been, as I brought with me the memories of my childhood, always there within me.

Papa Nico

"Nico" was what Mama called Papa when he came home for lunch on Saturdays with his white envelope still sealed and made a ritual of showing us children that he handed his wages to Mama. Navy-blue beret on his white head, still wearing the black smock he used to protect his everyday clothes, Papa entered the kitchen where the family convened, waved his envelope and announced, "We are going to celebrate today."

He pulled Mama away from the stove where she stood ready to throw in the pasta, and they danced together, twirling around. My oldest siblings and I laughed, pleased at such an intimate demonstration of affection, while the young ones, more timid, hid under the table, hugging its legs, covering their eyes.

"Nicolò" is what Mama called Papa when she smelled trouble, when she wanted him to really hear what she had to say, and when they discussed problems that were going to affect the whole family. "Nicolò" was our cue to listen, to pay attention to what was going on.

It was impossible not to listen to what was happening in our two-bedroom apartment. It was impossible not to get involved in everyone's business. Not only we children heard, but the neighbors and passersby heard what Mama and Papa talked about because Papa was almost deaf. So we all screamed at the top of our voices, frustrated from having to repeat the same sentence several times, while Mama, in the midst of our shouting match, would say, "*Mamma mia,* close the kitchen window. The neighbors are going to think we are a cage full of crazy people."

But Papa, untouched by such a display of frustration, would break the tension by saying, "But, why are you screaming? Do not shout like that.

Bella, repeat to me slowly what you want to say. I can hear. Just pronounce the words properly."

As Papa sat erect at the head of our big, marble-topped kitchen table, he would turn his head, eyes shining on us, and say, "Just talk normal, like me."

Often Papa would utter, "*Che bella famiglia!*" as he landed in his favorite chair.

"Aren't we lucky, Teresa, to have such a nice, big family?" turning to Mama, he would say. "*Si, bambini,* the family together. Remember, a united family is the most important thing in life."

"Isn't it true Anna that the family is important?" he'd ask, not really expecting an answer.

I jerked my neck a little to look at Papa, as I peered at my siblings out of the corner of my eyes, and said, "*Si,* Papa," and jumped out of my seat to kiss him.

"Anna, Gabri, Pietro, did you go and say hi to Uncle Paolo?" Papa asked. "Poor Uncle Paolo, he has no children. He would have liked to have children . . .Isn't it true, Teresa, that my brother Paolo would have liked to have six children like we do. Poor couple across the street. Do you see, *bambini,* how sad they look. Ten years they have been married and still no children. Poor people. Be kind to them!"

My papa thought himself the luckiest man on the island to have had six children. Yes, I thought he was lucky because he always said he was. Even though I understood that our family had kept his feet embedded on the cobblestones.

An incurable dreamer, if Papa had followed his instincts from time to time, he would have blasted off the *fondamenta,* jumped into a high-speed motorboat, and taken a few detours in the lagoon of Venice. Instead, he kept his dreams in the kitchen on top of the credenza. He stared at them, talked about them during and after dinner, and kept them alive in his mind while he savored with much gusto the now, and what he perceived to be the most important things in his life: a united family, friends, God and food. Not necessarily in that order.

The Family

Honorary Family Member holding the author

The Best Girl in Murano

Mama was quick in everything she did, as well as in choosing her man. At thirteen, she had fallen in love with Papa the first time she saw him while she stood outside her front door in the courtyard, her back against the wall watching some children playing.

Papa always said he remembered that day with clarity because Mama looked like an exotic beauty dressed in a summer white-gossamer dress. Her dark, long thick pigtail rested on one shoulder. Her high forehead with a widow's peak in the center and her prominent cheekbones were exposed in the fresh air, in the sunshine. Papa said he thought she was an apparition, a young *Madonna*.

"You are Signora Linda's daughter, aren't you?" Papa said to her.

Mama nodded.

"You are so beautiful. Some day, I'm going to marry you," he teased her.

Mama believed him. She thought he was serious. The problem was that he was thirteen years older than she and engaged to someone else. But when you fall in love, circumstances do not matter. Evidence of a fiancée did not faze Mama, either. She waited for ten years, hoping in the shadow of her own private thoughts that Papa would ask her out.

One day, when Mama was twenty-three, Papa waited for her outside the church and asked her if he could walk her home. He had to talk fast because the church was just a few meters from Mama's house. Papa asked her if he could walk with her in the early evening up and down the *fondamenta*.

"Yes," Mama said, "I would like that very much."

"Talk louder because I am deaf," Papa replied.

You might as well have slapped Mama in the face. That night she could not sleep as the words, "Talk louder because I'm deaf," churned in her mind with the same vigor her mother used to churn the spoiled milk to make butter out of it.

And Mama made butter out of those words.

She took them, and with her pragmatic reasoning turned them into, "I waited for this man to ask me out for more than ten years and I'm not going to let, 'Talk louder because I'm deaf' stand in my way."

And that was that.

At times, we teased Mama and told her that she married an old man, but she always took out the picture of their wedding day and, indeed, Papa at forty had been a handsome "old man." Thin, tall, with dark wavy hair, he looked smart in his blue suit, and radiant in the picture next to Mama dressed in white.

"I've married the best girl in Murano," Papa always uttered with conviction. "Isn't it true, Teresa? Yes, I married the best woman in Murano."

Indeed, everyone agreed that Mama was a lady, a very fine lady.

Nico and Teresa

Edible Gold

On special occasions, Mama baked a cake for the family with flour, eggs, sugar, and raisins. On the top, she designed abstract swirls with beaten egg whites and melted chocolate. Then she sprinkled crunchy ground-nuts on it, and after dinner, Mama gave us one small slice of cake.

Like a ritual, Papa whispered loud enough so that we all could hear, "Do not forget, Teresa, to cut a piece for Aunt Claretta, for Great Aunt Nice and for your sister Susi."

Even though we knew why our Mama always cut the slices in small portions, my siblings and I complained at the preposterous idea that when she made something special, we had to share it with other members of the family who did not even live in our same building and could not smell the scent of the cake while it baked.

Papa's sister, Aunt Claretta, always knew when Mama baked a cake, even if she lived on the other side of the island. She joked that Mama, with her teaching, swirled us like she did the batter of egg whites she designed on the top of her cake. Aunt Claretta was funny about baking. When she made a cake with one of Mama's recipes, she complained that hers did not taste the same as Mama's. But when Gelmina asked her if she had used the eight eggs, and the pound of butter like Signora Teresa did, she said with a sheepish look, "Well, to tell you the truth, I only used six eggs, and margarine instead of butter."

A comment that led Gelmina to roll her eyes and whisper, "See, I'm sure the cake looked the same as your Mama's, but . . .everything that shines is not really gold."

At times, Papa came home and told us children in a diction that implied surprise and wonder, as though he were talking about edible gold, "I bought some peanu-u-uts. After lunch, we are going to eat peanuts." He'd motioned for one of us to fetch the peanuts in the entrance hall where he had left them, to render the surprise more effective.

"Give them to Mama," he'd say with pride.

I could always tell how pleased Mama was that he found pleasure in sharing a bag full of peanuts when she said, "Thank you, Nico," while looking at Papa with eyes that looked like those of the fish she bought at the fish market on Fridays.

Our family had a lot of fun during dinner. We children often sang and danced trying to amuse Mama who, pleased to see us having fun, on occasion cracked a smile.

At home, I could easily forget the school's pressures, the small ups and downs, the growing pains, the feelings of insecurity I sometimes experienced with friends. My friends were important to me. I could not have imagined my life without them, in particular without my best friend Tina with whom I shared the vicissitudes of daily life.

At home I felt safe.

A Special Friendship

At twelve years of age, during summer vacation, I went to help Papa at his new mirror factory. At noon, when the vibrant sound of the bell towers resounded throughout the island, Papa said, "Let's go home to eat lunch. Let's go, Anna."

As we walked, holding hands, I peered at Papa from time to time to see if he looked old, if he lagged behind, if he showed signs of fatigue on his face. The August heat was hard on Papa. He wore his black working smock on top of his trousers, a short sleeved shirt, and a beige straw hat to protect his head from the scorching sun. Light traces of perspiration trickled slowly, crossing the horizontal lines on his old forehead. His round face and pensive eyes were imprinted with marks of fatigue from hard work.

Papa stooped when he walked, but he held his head up high so he could look people in their eyes. When Papa saw his friends, he called out to them, raising his hand in recognition.

"*Ciao*, Pieretto."

"Great friend, Pieretto," he'd said turning toward me. "We grew up together."

Papa talked about how much fun they had as young men when they went to the opera or to see Goldoni's comedies. Often, he told me a story like the one about Pieretto's wife.

"You see, Anna," Papa said, "Pieretto and I have a lot of respect for each other."

He paused for a moment, then spoke of when Pieretto's wife—the foreigner with a lot of education, who talked not in the Venetian dialect like everyone else, but in a high pitched Italian—took to gambling.

Everyone gossiped about her, about how much money she squandered, about how foolish Pieretto was for having married an outsider.

"All air," they used to say.

Papa told me how it hurt him to hear such rumbles about his friend's wife. One day, Papa waited for Pieretto and told him about his concerns. He advised Pieretto to try to help his wife.

"I told Pieretto," Papa's voice now a soft whisper, "that it saddened me to hear people talk about his wife."

When he said that, Papa turned and seemed to be looking for Pieretto.

"That was a special moment, a true moment of friendship. Oh, yes. Pieretto looked me in the eye, shook my hand, and said, 'Thank you, Nico.' Yes. He said that. Oh, yes."

As Papa talked, I remembered the time our family went to a family friend's house after dinner for dessert and coffee, and Signor Pieretto's family was there as well.

We sat around the rectangular, dark brown pine table in the center of a spacious room. The house looked like an Italian villa with terracotta painted walls covered with artwork of well-known Italian artists, like the *Accademia* Art Museum in Venice that we visited on special occasions. The Venetian *terrazzo* shined like one of the mirrors my brother Antonio and I cleaned at Papa's factory.

Papa and his friend Pieretto walked around the room scrutinizing the artwork, dropping artists' names as if they were overripe peaches from Gelmina's family farm. Mama talked to the foreigner who didn't look like she was having much fun, even though she smiled at everyone.

My older brother, Antonio, and I followed Papa around listening to what he had to say.

"Oh, look, Pieretto, how the color changes here as your eyes move from the foreground, the middle ground, to the background."

"*Si, si*. But, Nico, look how the artist uses, as his focal point, the figure in the middle, and how he reinforces his central position by placing the vanishing point just above his head."

They stopped in front of a *natura morta* and discussed how the reflected light fell on the fruits in the painting in such a way as to enhance the brilliance of the hues, thus giving the picture much life and lust. When Antonio and I heard Papa and Signor Pieretto mention names like Cubism,

Suprematism and Abstractism, we knew it was time to grab a *pasticcino* and sip on the hot espresso coffee the hostess had placed on the table when we came in.

After Papa and Signor Pieretto sat down and joined us, Signor Pieretto got up, put his hand on Papa's shoulder, and announced in a loud tone to everyone, but turning his head directly to face Papa, "Now, Nico is going to sing for us."

Eyes glistening with pride and clearing his voice, without hesitation Papa stood up and began to sing, "*Libiamo, libiamo ne'lieti calici che la bel-lez-za in fiora . . .* "

Everyone listened with respect to Papa's melodic but untrained voice.

When Papa finished singing, everyone clapped. Signor Pieretto positioned himself in back of Papa so that Papa could not read his lips, and with emotion Signor Pieretto said, "This is the nicest man anyone could possibly have for a friend. A man of much integrity."

Everyone became silent.

As Signor Pieretto's words dispersed through the room, I leaned towards my sister, Margherita, to touch her hand. I wondered if the foreigner felt the same way about Papa as her husband did. My youngest brother, Pietro, giggled, and we went on with the celebration.

Painting Dreams

Papa often told us how he paid for his youngest brother Andrea's education through hard work. He talked about reading on his own all of the books his brother Andrea, a Doctor in Letters and Science, read at the university. An avid reader, Papa tried to impart his knowledge to us when he had our undivided attention. He wished we had inherited his enthusiasm for books, music, art and history. He talked about great writers with such reverence as if they had been right there, seated at our table.

Papa was interested in people, the living as well as the dead. He introduced us to Machiavelli and said that he was not only a political and historical writer, but a comedy writer as well, with a keen understanding of the absurd, which he portrayed with brilliance in *La Mandragola*. Papa engaged us, especially Gabri, my oldest sister, who like Papa loved to read, in discussions about Dickens' *Great Expectations* and *A Tale of Two Cities* and said that through Dickens' books, we could view the moral and social conditions that mirrored the times Dickens represented.

Like a philosopher, he said, "*Bambini*, human nature doesn't change, only events and circumstances do. Oh yes, yes. . .*Bambini*, tomorrow go to the library and get a book by Dostoyevsky. He is a great writer. You'll see the intimacy with which he writes about people, about their conditions. See for yourself how he depicts the depth of their character. Oh yes, yes. Great writer, Dostoyevsky."

Papa sighed, paused, then added under his breath, "People said I should have gone to the university."

"He would have been a good student," Mama always concurred.

Papa told us of how he helped Uncle Andrea write his thesis. We all understood that Papa regretted not having attended school. Instead, he worked hard to help his mother and father put food on the table for the family while he himself dreamed and built memories.

"Your Papa is a dreamer," Aunt Claretta often said. "Even when he was young, I remember him painting in his mind his own little universe. Once he said he was depicting a garden with many colorful flowers which he called memories, and the sky with a multitude of bright little stars he called dreams." Aunt Claretta would smile, "What an imagination your Papa has!"

Papa talked about his dreams at the dinner table and told us that we must have dreams, too.

Papa dreamed about building a castle in the center of the Venetian lagoon. He had a clay prototype of a medieval castle on top of the pale green credenza in the kitchen, opposite from where he sat for lunch and dinner. It was a gift his friends made and presented to him one year on December 6, his saint's day, Saint Nicolò. They also gave him a poem written in Venetian dialect on parchment paper.

His friends constructed the castle with meticulous details. One could see the four towers in each corner of the tall ornate walls, a small bridge on the main gate to cross the moat on the outside, and many long, narrow windows on the circular stairways that led to the top of the towers.

"Some day, *bambini*, we are going to build a castle in the lagoon," Papa told us as he flourished his arms towards the castle.

We all liked the idea and played along.

"Papa, Papa," Margherita said, "I want three bathrooms in the castle so in the morning I do not have to wait in line outside the door."

"I want a big dining room," I said, "the biggest dining room and the biggest table so we can invite all of our friends over."

"Do not worry, Anna," Papa said. "You can have all the bathrooms you want, and the biggest table. I like tables. It's so nice to gather around the table. Isn't it true, Teresa?"

We talked about having huge parties, many servants, and cooks. We all. . .no, Mama was not a dreamer.

As we dreamed and played, Mama hid behind a veil of worries. She was the one who juggled the paycheck to make it last until the end of each week. Mama was always silent. She didn't partake in our fantasies. She didn't know whether to cry or laugh at the bursts of Papa's enthusiasm.

The castle represented quite a contrast to the two-bedroom apartment we lived in, and even more to the attic where Papa had lived with his mother, father and his six siblings as a young boy. But I understood that my Papa learned long ago that if you cannot feel the warmth of a fire you start with twigs, you can use your imagination and warm yourself with dreams. It worked for him. It worked for us children. It did not quite work for Mama.

Papa wanted a big family so we could have our own private soccer team and our own band. He wanted a big family so we could have a celebration around the kitchen table every day for lunch and dinner. I supposed Papa thought he didn't have enough children for a celebration because he invited just about everyone over to our house for lunch or dinner as he did on that very same day we had met Signor Pieretto.

Building Memories

Two strangers stopped us as I walked by Papa's side.

In the middle of the street stood two businessmen, a portly one and a thin, tall one, both dressed in light linen suits, uncertain of where to go. Papa moved towards them.

"Can I help you, gentlemen?" Papa said, his right hand cupped behind his ear, eyes fixed on their lips.

"Would you be so kind as to tell us where we can eat lunch? We would like to savor some specialty of Venetian cooking."

Papa reflected for a second while I stared at the two men.

"*Si,* wait a moment," he said.

Papa shifted his weight on his right foot, and leaned on my shoulder while he pondered what to do. He turned his head in all directions. He looked around, first to the right, then left, then on each side of the *fondamenta*. I waited, knowing well what Papa was going to tell the two gentlemen.

"I know the best place on the island. Follow me."

The two men smiled.

"Run home, Anna," Papa whispered in my ear as he leaned towards me, "Tell Mama I'm bringing two guests for lunch."

I ran across the *Ponte Lungo,* and dashed through *Fondamenta Cavour,* trying not to bump into people who, like me, were hurrying home.

I came face to face with one of Mama's friends who yelled at me, "Why are you running? Are you afraid your brothers will eat your pasta?"

I waved at her, but I kept on running. I had to tell Mama to add two extra plates.

The front door ajar, I entered. The aroma of fish frying on the stove reminded me it was Friday. I ran up the two flights of steps. My stomach growled. My mouth watered. I reveled in the thought that we were going to eat my favorite—*Risotto di Pesce*, fried sole and lettuce with a drop of the pure olive oil Papa's friend from Florence gave us every year in exchange for mirrors. Mama always prepared some sort of vegetable, fruit from the *Rialto* Market, wine from Gelmina's family farm, and espresso coffee.

Panting, I burst into the kitchen, walked towards the stove where Mama was standing, and tried to explain about Papa's two guests. For a moment I thought Papa's announcement surprised her.

"Are you sure they are strangers he met on the street?" Mama said. "Are you sure he doesn't know them?"

I nodded.

Mama sighed. "Who knows what he will come up with next," she said.

The kitchen window and the balcony door were open. The green and white striped awning that hung on the outside to protect us from direct sunlight extended into the open space. The red geraniums were in full bloom. The table was set with the customary white cotton tablecloth and napkins, glasses, the nine white ceramic dishes, forks and knives. A bottle of red wine sat on each side of the table and next to them two pitchers of fresh tap water. Wooden chairs sat around the kitchen table. My siblings stood in the kitchen chatting while Mama fried the fish and Gelmina stirred the risotto.

"Please, Gelmina, put two extra dishes on the table," Mama said.

Gelmina smiled. She left the wooden mixing spoon on the counter, walked to the credenza and placed the two extra place settings on the table. She approved of Papa and of his generosity.

On the table, Mama placed a bouquet of fresh flowers which her Great Aunt Nice gave her every week from her garden.

"Make sure that before you take a second helping, the guests are well fed," Mama warned us.

We nodded. We knew there were not going to be second helpings.

"Your Papa just does not understand," Mama sighed.

But like Aunt Claretta always said, Papa was good at stroking little flowers on the canvas of his life because he understood the importance of friendship, even with strangers. He was relentless in his pursuit to introduce us to people from different walks of life.

When the two strangers entered, all decked out in the latest fashion, jackets buttoned and ties fastened, my siblings and I were already seated.

"Teresa, Gelmina, *bambini*," Papa introduced us, "this is Signor Carlo and Signor Mario."

"Signori," he added, turning to the two men, "this is my family."

"*Piacere, piacere, piacere. . .*" back and forth went eight times two *piacere*, and when all the *piacere* were exhausted, we all sat down to eat lunch.

Shy at first, the two men, turning to Mama, said, "Signora, we are sorry to disturb you and your family and to intrude."

Mama smiled. "We are happy to have you. Please, do start eating."

The two strangers sat on the chairs on each side of Papa, and as we shared our meal, we listened to Papa as he uttered, "You see what a beautiful family I have. *Allegria. Allegria.*"

First came the *Risotto di Pesce,* a Venetian specialty, made of boiled fish, garlic, celery, and carrots, cooked to a creamy consistency in olive oil, butter, rice, parsley and parmesan cheese. Then, the fried sole and yellow *polenta* that melted in your mouth, and last the salad, the cooked tomatoes and basil, fresh fruits and coffee.

We children dipped our bread in the olive oil left on our plates from the salad and the fried fish, cleaning our dishes to a shiny luster. Mama, the disciplinarian in the family, like a sergeant, whispered, "Pietro, take your elbow off the table. . .Margherita, sit straight. Anna, pass the dish to Signor Carlo."

Signor Mario and Signor Carlo were brothers. They lived in Milano with their respective families where they owned a factory in which they manufactured wool sweaters, hats, gloves and coats. They, too, had six siblings in their family, and like Papa during The Depression, ate nothing but *polenta*. They, too, overcame much hardship, and were now trying to expand and modernize the family business their father began, peddling from house to house, selling the sweaters their mother had made by hand.

With the meal almost over, Signor Mario and Signor Carlo took off their jackets, untied their colorful ties, pushed their chairs away from the table, and assumed an air of familiarity as if we had been long time friends. They quizzed us like detectives as the scorching sun hit on the striped curtain, and the music from Signora Rosa's radio came bursting in like a tornado disrupting the harmony of the conversation.

Before they left, Signor Mario and Signor Carlo kissed us on both cheeks with great affection. Papa never saw nor talked to them again, but that year, at Christmastime, we received a large package, in it, nine sweaters, one for each member of the family. Each sweater had one of our names pinned on it, and a short note of thanks.

A Special Secret

When Mama's good friend, Signora Lola, came to visit Mama, she talked of when she and Mama were young.

"Do you remember, Teresa, how we walked on the *fondamenta* from one bridge to the next, back and forth, back and forth?"

As she spoke, we children listened with great curiosity, for she always added as if she were telling a big secret, "The girls walked on one side of the *fondamenta,* the boys across the canal on the other. We never tired of walking and talking as we eyed the boys."

She said that with a bright smile, her teeth as white as the keys of an accordion. Signora Lola made sure we understood that the "Walking and talking as we eyed the boys," was their special secret, the same secret everyone learned to act out as they grew up in Murano.

There was something peculiar about walking up and down the *fondamenta* as you could choose to see what you wanted to, and no more.

If you didn't want to talk to anyone, you could walk on the *fondamenta,* serious gaze fixed on the cobblestones, as if you worried that Murano would sink and disappear right under your feet. Or you could pretend you did not see the friend who strutted from the opposite direction in plain view of the whole world, nor the one walking on the other side of the canal. Nor the woman who shook the dust from her rug into the canal water, or hung her clothes on her clothesline. Most important, you could make yourself invisible by pretending to be *soprapensiero*—a state of mind that reigns beyond the sphere of any earthly thoughts.

When you walked in your reveries on the *fondamenta*, if someone called your name aloud, you could act surprised and say with a smile, "*Scusa*, I did not see you. I was *soprapensiero*."

If you had had a bad day at the factory, or your son got an F on his math test because the teacher said the child was a *deficiente*, you could pretend to be *soprapensiero*. Except that in doing so, you ran the risk of people reading into your unfriendly, preoccupied demeanor the possibility of a dark secret that for sure everyone would discover before you reached home.

It was the most natural thing among the small community of Murano to inquire, to confer, and to participate in everyone's sorrows or joys. It was normal for people on the street to talk to each other about their families or of someone else's.

Signora Lena, who lived across from the church, knew there was cause for worry when Signora Nella came out of the church's front door by herself, *soprapensiero*.

When Signora Valeria happened to pass Signora Lena's house, Signora Lena said, "Valeria, do me a favor. Tell me, what is wrong with Nella? She came out of the church and did not wave like she always does. Did something happen to her family?"

"I don't know," Signora Valeria said, as she placed her shopping bag on the pavement, one arm akimbo. She placed the other arm on Signora Lena's shoulder, repeating as if to herself, "I don't know. Perhaps she is worrying about her sister-in-law, Sandra."

"What happened to Sandra?"

"Don't you know? Just yesterday, someone told me that the *Pronto Soccorso* came, and they took her to the hospital in Venice."

"Are you talking about Sandra Cosato, married to Nella's oldest brother? Really? This morning I went to Venice, and I saw Sandra on the boat. She did not look sick to me. In fact, she was carrying a big grocery bag. I think she went to Rialto, to the market." Signora Lena conveyed in her musical trebles, heightened by waving her arms and hands.

"Well, this is what I heard. This is what Aida told me. You know Aida, she knows everything."

"But I'm worried about Nella," Signora Lena said. "Something must have happened to her to come out of the church at this time of day. Look, it's almost twelve. She goes to church every morning around eight-thirty, not at twelve when her husband comes home from work and lunch should be on the table."

Signora Lena folded the front of her cotton dress, one side onto the other, and tied the belt in a knot in the back. She looked up at the window right above her head. Signora Carla, hearing Signora Lena's voice, poked her head out of her window and listened to the conversation, resting her elbows on the marble windowsill.

"Isn't it true, Carla, that Nella looked rather sad today?" Signora Lena said, looking up at Signora Carla.

"I really did not notice, Lena," Signora Carla said.

"Ladies, go home to cook instead of lingering in the middle of the street like *comari*," Signor Sergio shouted as he hurried by.

"Look," Signora Lena said, pointing toward Signor Sergio who had already crossed the bridge and stopped to say hi to Father Michele.

"Sergio, Sergio," Signora Lena called, "He is right. Let's go home. I still have to set the table."

"*Ciao*, Lena."

" *Ciao*, Valeria."

"*Si, Si.* We'll see you."

That is how, in Murano, one found out about people. One word here, one word there, and everyone knew, or assumed they knew, what went on. Like it or not, people talked about each other. If they saw you beaming, frowning, skipping, bouncing, running, or walking, they talked about you. People repeated to you things others said about you. If they thought you were dumb, and then found out you were actually very capable, they believed they were paying you a great compliment when they said to your face, "Wow, you are a fast learner! Your cousin said you were a retard." Or, "We all thought you were a big *stupido*, instead. . ."

As you walked through the *fondamenta* and just glanced at people's facial expressions and demeanor, you could weave many interesting stories with a little imagination. If the *Muranesi* saw an ambulance pass by and thought they saw Lino the baker on a stretcher half dead, by the time Lino reached the hospital the news would have spread though Murano. According to the voices of Murano, Lino could have died of a heart attack, acquired a deadly disease, drowned in a rain or wind-storm in the lagoon, got sick because someone saw him eat raw clams and drink icy cold beer. Or he could have drowned in fifty liters of water he drank during the day due to the scorching heat.

People told many stories, and for the most part, they were true. Albeit, they weaved them with a wide range of embroidery contrived with the same creativity the artisans of Murano used to create their artistic glass works.

Silvio Tan Tan

A Walk Through Murano

One day, in the sweet aura of dusk, facing the lenient autumn wind and wrapped in a heavy, green wool sweater, I walked from Papa's mirror factory towards *Ponte Lungo* to meet my best friend Tina. Prancing in and out of people's way, I looked at people to see if they noticed me, or if they waved so that I could wave back.

I turned into *Calle Dietro gli Orti*, and watched the workers coming out of Riotto's glass factory. I trailed close to the two young men I often noticed on the street and listened to their conversation.

"Can you keep a secret," asked the blond one.

"What? *Dai, Dai, che segreto. . .Spua.*"

"Come on, come on, what secret...spit it out," said the one with long eyebrows glued in a long strip of furry bristles.

"My father and I are going to start a small side business in our house. We'll work in the evening. I'll keep half of the profits."

"Do you want to know something?" replied the thick-browed one, "I already knew it." He placed his two thumbs on each side of his temples and flapped his fingers up and down. "I already knew it. . .I already knew it."

"How did you know?" A rhetorical question which the blond one should not have asked. He should have known that in Murano, even if a secret were at its genesis, or a figment of one's imagination, someone, somewhere, already knew about it. It seemed to me, that if one were telling a secret, one could wait until one reached a deserted or secluded place, just like Tina and I often did.

I moved closer to the two young men, but they stopped talking to each other and started teasing another worker, an elderly man who looked, I thought, a bit like my father—with a few pounds to spare, rosy complexion, smiling eyes, salt and pepper hair.

I turned the corner onto *Fondamenta dei Vetrai*, one of the main walking arteries in Murano. Many people stood talking. The warm, artificial glow of the shop lights fused onto the *fondamenta* through the small gaps that separated the people socializing with one another. The hiatus between people often bridged with a handshake, a warm embrace, the gesticulation of the hands, a kind, sympathetic word, or a futile insult.

I reveled in the warmth of electrical lights reflecting in the canal water that gave the small island a sense of fantasy.

I looked through the well-lit window of Signor Rino's shop to see if his old father was still seated on the chair in front of the red curtain that divided the front part of his shop from the storage room.

Signor Rino's shop had been there for many years. It belonged to his mother and father, and now that his mother was dead, and his father was getting older, he and his wife managed the shop. Mama liked to buy linen at Signor Rino's shop for our dowries, even if we were still young. Money was a scarce commodity in our family, and most weeks Mama had to stretch it like she stretched the elastic in our skirts. Mama thought that to acquire fine linens, table-wares, and wool blankets was a good investment. No one would use these items for a long time. She would have to store them on the last shelf of the already crowded armoire in our bedroom. But it was a way to save, to make some progress as a family.

Mama paid Signor Rino a small amount every week, but no one in Murano was supposed to know it. She had sworn us to secrecy because her own mother and father never bought anything on credit, and she felt embarrassed to have to pay with small installments.

"I'll buy a little at a time, and before you know it, you'll all have as nice a dowry as my mother gave me," she said with the same trepidation in her voice as when she told us it was our family's secret to buy on credit.

I knew that Mama did not want people to say, as they did with Signora Alba, that she gave her children nothing but rags when they began their new married life. For Mama, who grew up in a comfortable household, where her parents bought nothing but the best, what people thought about her family was important.

Now, people were parading on each side of the canal, stopping to say hello as a final splash of sunrays plunged behind the buildings and into the lagoon, in their last dive before nightfall. Workers returned home after a long, arduous day at the glass factories. Some were last minute shoppers who popped in and out of grocery stores, milk stores, bread stores, tobacco stores and meat stores, which all remained open until seven-thirty.

Like everyone else in Murano, I thought myself very lucky to live on a small island. There were no cars to pollute the air. You could cross, run or hop over the bridges any time of night or day without having to worry about cars traveling at full speed, or drunken drivers flying over from the other side of the canal. You did not have to stop for traffic signals or at stop signs.

The islanders felt blessed that they could live in peace and raise a family away from the crime of a big city. Protected by the island's geography, which had sheltered them from outsiders for centuries, the islanders worked hard to preserve their status quo.

I took a few more steps and saw Aunt Claretta's husband, Uncle Nano, outside the *osteria* with his friends. Every evening, rain or shine, they stopped at the *osteria*, and as they played cards, they teased each other, talked about politics, and told stupid jokes about communism, Lenin and Stalin. They always drank a glass of wine and ate a *cichetto*—a small snack that is supposed to entice one's appetite.

Uncle Nano saw me walking by.

"Are you going home?" he said. "*Brava,* say hi to your Mama for me."

Uncle Nano looked so different from Papa.

He was taller than Papa. His large forehead folded into a shining head, and his big nose stood out like a dotted, red bell pepper. To make us laugh, Gelmina used to say under her breath that Uncle's ears could sail and keep him afloat during a thunder storm in the Atlantic Ocean.

I went to kiss Uncle Nano on the cheek.

I was glad I could kiss him because just two years before, he and Papa had a misunderstanding. Papa had been a partner at the big glass factory that Uncle now owned.

We knew Mama had been distressed the day Papa announced at the kitchen table that he wanted out of the partnership.

"Nicolò," Mama had said without any advance warning, "are you sure you want to take this step all on your own? The children are still little," she added with trepidation in her voice. "What would we do if the new company fails? How would we feed the children? Perhaps your brother Paolo is right. Stay put for a while longer."

Mama had worried, and we children had worried, too.

Most of all we worried about losing Cousin Silvana's friendship. We felt sick at the thought of not being able to go over to Aunt Claretta and Uncle Nano's house to eat, as well as being able to greet them when we met on the street. We. . .

A small motorboat swished by at full speed, generating big waves. The noise distracted everyone, but only for a few seconds.

I said goodbye to Uncle Nano and walked on.

Silvio *Tan-Tan*, a huge older man with white hair, a large face, a jutting double chin, and three rolls of lard around his waist that he hid under his white vest, motioned for me to stop. Silvio was one of Papa and Mama's best friends and one of my eleven godparents. *Tan-Tan* was a nickname he had acquired during his youth when he sang with exuberance, together with his friends, the Triumphal March of Aida to the tune of *Tan tan, ta ra tan tan, tan, tan, ta ra tan tan tan tan. . ..* When he saw me, Signor Silvio *Tan-Tan* stopped talking to his customers.

"I just saw your brother, Antonio, going home," he said. "Are you hungry?"

He turned around and with a colander fished a small, bright pink octopus out of a huge metal cylindrical container filled with steamy boiling water. He placed it on a small, white ceramic dish, and added a dash of salt, pepper and a tablespoon of olive oil. Holding the plate with his big furry hands, handed it to me. I wanted to gulp down the octopus, but I chewed it because Mama always said that one must not devour everything without savoring it.

"You go home now. Say hi to Nico," Silvio *Tan Tan* said when I finished.

Silvio *Tan Tan* was one of Murano's landmarks. Every day he stood on the *fondamenta* under the awning of the *trattoria* by the *Ponte di Mezzo* with his ambulant container, and sold his delicious octopus, *scampi*, and crab, when in season.

Next door to Silvio *Tan-Tan* was the *Pasticceria,* my favorite store in Murano, which had a shiny marble floor, and an elegant orange and black granite countertop. The fancy shop lifted my spirit every time I went by. It had a huge pastry display and its wall of shelves from the ceiling to the floor was decked with every piece of pastry one's imagination could fathom.

I could not help but pause for a moment at the *Pasticceria's* window and glance inside while the smells grabbed my stomach the same way as when Aunt Susi, Mama's younger sister, invited the family to her house and made us pick from a tray full of Alfio's pastries, even offering us a second one. However, at Aunt Susi's, Mama looked at us with severe eyes, forcing us to say, "No, thank you. I do not feel like having another piece."

Alfio, the *pasticcere,* popped in and out of the kitchen. With his ebony hair slicked back, and his sharp pointed chin, he resembled more of a caricature than a real person. He held, like an oracle with the palm of his hand extended up in the air, trays full of pastries. He never said hi to anyone, nor smiled. He'd just nod his head in recognition.

Alfio and his wife, "poor people," did not have any children. However, they did have a feisty little dog that looked like a white fur ball that spun around, sweeping the gleaming marble floor. As the dog yapped, it charged at the customers. And if Alfio did not grab and carry the dog into the back room, the dog jumped and tore at customers' socks with its sharp teeth.

A few steps away from the *Pasticceria,* facing *Ponte di Mezzo,* the fruit vendor, my friend Renzo, and his father, cleaned and sorted vegetables and fruits all day. It seemed to me like an easy job to stand behind a counter and greet the customers who came in to buy their produce, but it was not. Every morning Renzo and his father got up at four o'clock, and went to the *Rialto* Market in Venice in their motorboat, where merchants bought their produce. They went there five days a week, even during the rainy season or in winter when the temperature was several degrees below zero and big chunks of ice floated in the canal.

At the foot of the bridge, I stopped for a moment to wave to my friend Renzo.

A young, screaming mother, reprimanded her curly-haired toddler who was running up the bridge and down to the other side out of her view.

"Come here. Stay right here. Do not move. Do you want to fall in the canal? I'm not going to save you. If you fall, *peccato*. I'll tell your father when he comes home from the factory if you do not behave."

Her words were louder than Rita Pavone's, a popular singer, whose recorded voice came from a second floor open window where an older lady was hanging her clothes. No doubt, the lady hoped the damp breeze would dry her garments before the sun disappeared, and the moon spun through the sky, displaying her translucent gown.

On the other side of *Ponte di Mezzo*, the baker in his white jacket stood guard at the door of his *Panetteria* talking to the man who sold nails, hammers, screwdrivers, and light bulbs. The two friends waved their hands about as they discussed the weather, teased passersby and cracked jokes.

I crossed the bridge and walked towards *Ponte Lungo*. At the beginning of *Viale Garibaldi* a small, green wooden *chiosco* stood open. Behind the counter, a communist, Dario Miao, sold sweets. Dario Miao had acquired his nickname when he "miaoed, miaoed" to tease the girls who came to buy his candies. A variety of candies in all shapes and colors were displayed in thick, rectangular transparent glass jars.

As I walked on, to my right stood a three-story villa surrounded by a prolific garden. A round fish-fountain adorned the front garden. Two green benches where Mama's family used to gather on limpid spring and summer nights sat on each side of the path. Great Aunt Nice and Aunt Susi still lived on the ground floor. Uncle Ruggero, Aunt Lina and cousin Adriana lived on the second one. They all guarded and maintained the yard with the same accuracy my Great-Grandfather Giuseppe used to keep it.

I increased my pace when I saw Franca, Mama's second cousin, coming from behind. I didn't feel like talking to her. But Franca caught up with me at the *portico* with the gothic style windows.

"Ciao, Anna. How is the family? How is your Mama? I heard your Papa has started a new business," Franca said, without breathing.

Franca was very good at asking questions, better than the priests from the Spanish Inquisition I had studied in school. And like in the Inquisition, if I did not answer fast enough, Franca made up the answers herself.

As we passed by the church, I fixed my eyes on the cobblestones and pretended to be looking at my shoes. I felt guilty that I did not go to confession and take communion on the previous Sunday, and I was afraid that if I met the Monsignor, he would reprimand me in front of Franca.

We approached the *Ponte Lungo*. I strained to see if my friend Tina was in front of the cafè at the foot of the bridge waiting for me. Franca said goodbye and rushed to help a young mother lift a baby carriage to the other side of the bridge.

The sound of a horn startled me. A young man rowing solo in a long, yellow kayak was intersecting a cargo boat carrying lumber. For a moment I thought they might collide. The navigators of the cargo yelled, and the kayak got out of the way just in time.

Tina stood at the bottom of the bridge waiting for me to cross over. When I finally stood by her side, she clutched her hand under my arm.

"Do you like my shoes?" she said. "They are new."

"Your feet hurt," I asked.

"Yes," she said.

We could read each other's minds. At once, we exchanged shoes. Arm in arm, we pranced towards the cemetery, uncaring of what went on around us, enjoying our time together. Our relationship was like the one Papa had with Uncle Paolo: best friends, we all shared many things throughout our lives with the same spontaneity Tina and I shared our shoes.

The Facts of Life

Often, my friend Tina and I dashed like two crickets through the field of wild grass to the cemetery. We sat on the bottom step by the green entrance gate. We talked about our families, our lives, and our papas.

It felt good talking with Tina. It helped us to uncork our emotions and let them soar all around in the silence of the moment.

As night fell on the dark cement path, the flow of visitors dwindled. At closing time, the guardian of the cemetery came to lock the gate.

"Good evening, young ladies," he said as he disappeared behind the tall boxwood hedge growing on each side of the gate.

One particular early evening, Tina and I walked to the cemetery as usual.

"Today I went to help my father," Tina said.

"What did you do," I asked.

"My mother, Elisa, and I wrapped glasses all day," Tina answered. "My whole family was there."

"Your aunt, uncle, and grandmother?"

"Papa needed help," Tina said. Then almost to herself, she added, "He needs the money. In the last few months he has sent many parcels out, but no one has paid."

I knew what Tina meant. My Papa, as well, had walked back and forth to all of the stores in Venice, hoping they would pay him for the mirrors he supplied them. The last time he went, Papa came home again with no money.

"I told one of the vendors," Papa had said to Mama, "that he would have to pay for a new set of shoes if I had to go back one more time."

Mama forced herself to laugh.

"I added to the bill two thousand lire for a new pair of soles," Papa continued. I sensed that he said that to cheer up Mama, but Mama's laugh was fringed with disappointment.

I looked at Tina and wished in my heart that her papa's factory made some money. I tried to remember the exact day we first met, but I could not. Our thread of friendship extended beyond the pendulum of our lifetime. Our grandmothers and mothers had gone to the same kindergarten and elementary school as we did. They had shared the most important moments of their lives together.

Like our mothers, Tina and I did everything together. We walked to school, to church. We walked all over Murano. We bought candy at our favorite candy store, Dario Miao, with our small allowance. Sometimes we earned money selling to our relatives the snails we gathered after the rain in the church field. We played with our friends at the church ground after school or under the cloisters of *San Pietro Martire* Cathedral. We often wandered to those parts of Murano where young girls should have feared to venture. We sat on the bridge to count our collection of postcards two old spinsters had given us on the thirty-first of May. Tina and I had gone to Mass at seven every morning before school to show our devotion to the Virgin Mary, so that was our reward.

Some of the postcards had shiny glitter all over them. Others had peaceful scenes of flowers, lakes, mountains, rivers and trees. The postcards represented a life-time of memories, each engraved with a meaningful message. We miss you. We are having fun. Wish we were spending Christmas with you. We are thinking of you.

Often, Tina and I meandered through the *fondamenta,* in and out of *calli* and *campi,* up and down the *Ponte Lungo, Ponte di Mezzo* and *Ponte Santa Chiara.*

We walked to forbidden corners of the island, even after Mama's friend, Signora Lena, told us that if we took one step past the lighthouse, or went to the cemetery after dark, people would put a *tabarro* over our heads and shoulders. When I asked Mama what her friend meant, she explained that a *tabarro* was a dark, imaginary mantle made up of people's gossips.

"If you are a young girl of twelve," Mama said, "you would rather not wear it as it means people consider you *poco de bon*, loose. Once people put the *tabarro* on you, you would never be able to take it off, even if it were one hundred degrees outside."

At twelve, Tina and I were too young to comprehend the seriousness of the implication. We were too innocent to consider not walking towards the forbidden areas as all we wanted to do was talk about our girlfriends and boys.

When Signora Lena saw us walking towards the lighthouse at six o'clock on a dark winter evening, she called, startling us.

"Do you see that bridge?" she said, pointing her index finger towards the church bridge.

"Do you see the other bridge?" she added, turning in the opposite direction, still keeping her bare hand high in the cold air.

Tina and I turned our heads, first left, then right. We looked at her, not really understanding what she wanted. We did not dare look at each other for we might have burst into laughter.

"When your mothers and I were your age," Signora Lena said, arching her brows, "we could not go beyond those two bridges by ourselves. People would have talked about us and would have thought we were up to no good."

She shook her head as if it were our fault that her world was coming to an end just because Tina and I could walk beyond the two bridges with impunity.

"Go home, *bambine*. It's late. Go home before someone sees you," she implored as she opened her mouth, full of dark stained teeth.

We ran. We charged in and out of all the last minute shoppers, and the workers going home from the glass factories. We passed the lit glass windows of the bread store, the fruit store, the appliance store, the flower shop, and the barber-shop without searching for our reflections. We tried to suppress our giggles so that Signora Lena could not hear us. When we came to the church bridge, we stopped by the lion faced *fontana* to drink from the dribble of fresh water that spurted from its mouth. Only then did we laugh so hard that tears ran down our red cheeks.

"Do you think anyone saw us?" we chanted as we pointed our index fingers at each other.

"Really, your mother is going to. . .ha, ha, ha,"

Deep down we knew that by the time we got home, our mothers would already know our whereabouts. In Murano there was no place to hide. Someone, somewhere, was always looking.

Murano's inhabitants had the innate gift of reading your mind. They knew who was having an affair and the precise moment people fell in love. They knew how people got sick and died, who was born and at what time. They knew all of the particulars of each other's lives. What they did not know, they made up. Events turned, within an instant, into a secret tale everyone whispered about. News germinated and multiplied from one end of the island to the other faster than bacteria could breed. Perhaps it was the humid climate, perhaps it was the density of the population of twelve thousand, but that was how people interacted with one another. Even the purchase of your new red shoes or your new woolen hat made the front page of the verbal morning paper.

I knew that if my cousin, Rose, walked through the *Fondamenta Venier* with her best friend, a widow, and they happened to meet a tall, handsome young man, and Rose's friend blushed as the young man mouthed a *"ciao!"* to her and lowered his gaze at the precise moment in which their paths crossed, that meant they liked each other. But if later on that same afternoon, Rose's husband found himself on the train to Mestre, eye to eye with the same young man, and Rose's husband had just been informed that Rose's best friend had recently bought a house in Mestre for her son, and the house was still empty, it was a given that the young man and my cousin's widow friend were having a love affair.

If I told Mama I was going to the beach with Tina and my other friends, and there we met a group of young boys and had fun and joked together all day, and when it was time to go home one of them grabbed my hand to help me run faster so I would not miss the last boat to Murano, the first question Mama would ask as I entered the kitchen was not, "Did you have fun?" but, "Who was the boy who grabbed your hand at the boat station?"

It was no use for me to act surprised, to raise my eyebrows and beg Mama to tell me who her informer was because Mama would always answer, "One can reveal the sin, the sinner, but never tell on the informer."

Muranesi were skilled in storytelling as well. If they did not like the real version of a story, they invented their own rendition. Mothers, especially, had great imaginations. They had the ability to make a wrong a right by minimizing their children's indiscretions with trivial excuses. They would explain with fastidious details their own version of a situation, fooling themselves into thinking that people would actually believe their fantastic account of an event.

Tina and I learned many facts of life listening to people's stories, albeit, often in the wrong order.

That is how Tina and I learned that in Murano there were many Virgin Marys who had conceived their children without ever having sex. It should not have been a hard story to believe. Our mothers, grandmothers, grandmother's mothers, and everyone else in Murano believed that Jesus' birth came about through a miracle, and that Mary was still a virgin when she became pregnant with Him. The priest, during catechism, spent hours on the subject trying to make everyone understand the miracle—an unnecessary practice because the whole population of Murano was born thinking the matter a fact of life.

Ignorant of how babies came about, one cannot be surprised to know that Tina and I were confused the day we heard Rosina and Antonia talking on the cemetery steps. Our ears perked up when Antonia walked out of the cemetery with her friend Rosina, and stopped at the top step, right by our side. Tina and I sat still against the wall, holding our breath, trying to look invisible.

Antonia bent her knees, leaned forward, and with her double chin almost touching her big breasts, she moved her right arm back and forth from her forehead and back into the open air, her five fingers closed together.

"Tell me," Antonia said, stressing her tone of voice to a high pitch, "Tell me, Rosina, how unlucky can she be? Tell me if she could not have been more unlucky?"

For each "tell me" Rosina looked at Antonia, nodding in assent. All fired up, Antonia, kept repeating how unlucky her daughter was. How she believed her because she knew that her daughter had never, ever lied to her before.

Tina and I, mouths agape, kept silent, waiting to find out what her daughter had "not" done.

Antonia stopped. She moved her right foot sideways, as if to dig her shoes deep into the cobblestones, as if she were to make history right by the cemetery's front door. In a solemn movement, she brought her hand in front of her, palm extended upwards, fingers closed together, looking intently at her own gestures as if to make sure Rosina understood this sacred moment. She placed the tip of her thumb hard into the first crease of the phalange of her index finger and pushed the thumb-nail upward, stopping one quarter of an inch from the top.

"Look, look here," Antonia said. "This far he pushed into it. Only just this far. Can you believe it? Poor kid. No sex. She did not have sex. Just this far and she got pregnant."

When Antonia and Rosina slowly walked away, Tina and I got up and ran around the corner. We laughed our heads off for ten minutes but never discussed the matter again.

We did not have to. By the time the day was over everybody was uttering, "Did you hear about. . . Can you believe. . ." Everyone talked about the two young adults who had to get married because she was pregnant, even though they did not have sex. In most of the accounts, the word sex was not mentioned to protect innocent children, who, like Tina and me, understood half of what they heard. We understood the other half via a different story. That day, Antonia taught us that one had to push "it" all the way into "it" to have sex.

However, we learned how a baby came out of a mother's body at a different time.

One day after school, I asked Tina if she could walk home with me. Every day, a boy, a few years older than we were, waited at the third floor window of his apartment building and spat insults at me. I did not know him personally. I knew him because his mother was second cousin to my father's sister's husband, and during the summer, he worked at the store where my mother bought her groceries. I saw him behind the counter as he flirted, teased, and joked with every woman, young and old, who entered the grocery store.

"*Varda che bela che la ze ancuo! Che bel vestito! E che paruca!*" "How beautiful you are today. What a pretty dress. And what a hairstyle."

When he made a joke, he looked at me with his bright blue eyes to see if I heard him. I pretended I did not hear him and looked elsewhere. I never said hi to him on the street because no one had introduced us.

Every day, when I entered *Calle Conterie* on my way home from school, he waited for me.

"Barrel, barrel. You are so fat," he chanted, one hand cupped around his mouth, the other on the window-frame.

Each time my stomach turned into one big tangled knot. My imagination ran amuck as I envisioned myself running up the stairs, barging into his apartment and kicking him.

Instead, I just walked straight ahead, books under my arm. I never answered him back or acknowledged his presence. But I wanted to stick my tongue out at him. That's why one day I asked Tina to come with me for moral support.

Tina had a spunky personality. If something bothered her, everyone knew it. She had no problem sticking her tongue out at this boy. When she did, I felt smart and found the courage to call him *deficiente,* mentally deficient. Then we ran as fast as we could towards my house.

Before we reached it, we heard a scream and muffled loud voices coming from the semi-closed green wooden shutters of a first floor apartment we were passing. Heads popped out of the windows on the upstairs floor, and a few people came running toward the door.

"It's Giulietta. It's Giulietta."

"It's time for her to have her baby."

"Run, someone go and call the midwife."

As Tina and I approached, the voices became louder and louder.

"What's happening," people asked each other.

"*Mama, Mama, Mama mia.* I'm sick, I'm dying, I'm dying. I'm dying!" Giulietta screamed from inside.

The people on the outside shouted at Giulietta to stay calm and lie on the bed. They pounded on the door and told Giulietta's mother to open it. Tina and I tried to sneak in front of the line. When the midwife came and the door opened, we wanted to look at Giulietta who was having a baby, who was dying from pain.

"Look at her. Look at how she screams. Push, push," Giulietta's husband screamed. "The doctor said you have to push, to push."

The door remained shut.

The neighbors shook their heads while arguing about poor Giulietta.

"It's the mother's fault," they whispered.

When Giulietta was a young adult, every day mother and daughter dressed up in their finest. Heads held up high, arm in arm, they click-clacked, click-clacked in their high-heeled shoes down *Calle del Mistro*, through the *Fondamenta Cavour*, to catch the five o'clock boat to Venice.

Giulietta and her mother looked so proud. Her mother talked in a high pitch to Giulietta to make sure Giulietta understood what she was saying. Giulietta looked into space, no one knew where for both her eyes crossed in the center. You could not tell if she stared at you or if she looked at the other side of the canal. On the way to Venice, her mother coached her.

"Be nice to that young little blond we met yesterday," she said to Giulietta. "I think he likes you."

While her mother talked, Giulietta repeated the last few words of each sentence, "Be nice, he likes you."

Giulietta was a bit simple. She followed her mother's instructions and married the young blond chef, a drunk, who spent all of his free time drinking and singing from one *Osteria* to the next. He married Giulietta, and the three of them set up house in the one room studio apartment.

Tina and I stood outside Giulietta's apartment waiting to see what would happen. We were scared. I wanted to cry and run home, but my feet did not move.

"*La se qua! La se qua!*" "She is here! She is here!" someone shouted from the back of the huge crowd who now stood outside Giulietta's door.

The midwife pushed her way through till she reached the door. She tapped at it several times as she implored Giulietta's mother to open it.

Inside the studio apartment, Giulietta moaned.

The door opened wide enough for the midwife and another woman to pass through. When the door shut, a neighbor told everyone to go home and pray. With reluctance, Tina and I walked to my house where everyone already knew what had happened.

"Poor, poor, Giulietta," Mama said in a whisper as if she were reflecting. "It's best if we say a little prayer for her and the baby."

With all those people praying, you would think that things could have turned out better.

The neighbor who locked up Giulietta's apartment after Giulietta was taken to the hospital said that when the midwife entered, Giulietta was lying in bed without any clothes, legs spread wide open. She was crying and pushing the baby's dark, furry head back in.

The baby wanted out, but Giulietta pushed it right back in.

Blood was on the white sheets, on the floor, on the walls, and all over Giulietta's naked body. The mid-wife took Giulietta's bloody hands away and pulled the baby out. The other lady held Giulietta down with force, helped by the mother and Giulietta's husband, who were still arguing.

The walking ambulance arrived.

Giulietta was rushed to the hospital.

Four men, carrying a stretcher, had docked the water boat ambulance at the end of *Calle San Donato*. They came running towards Giulietta's room at a frantic pace. People ran after them. Everyone along the way stood at their balconies and doorways waiting for Giulietta to pass by. Some hid behind curtains, some stood right outside of their doors wanting to give Giulietta moral support and a few words of encouragement. It was their way to show they cared and to let Giulietta know that they prayed for her, even if most of them had never talked to her before.

When she went by, Giulietta was unconscious. The four paramedics held the stretcher's poles and a tube to her mouth. The midwife ran by her side, holding Giulietta's hand. As Giulietta's husband and her mother trailed behind screaming, everyone thought Giulietta and the baby. . . dead.

Giulietta was not dead. Her baby was.

The voices of Murano whispered for a long time that the doctors in the hospital "Made sure Giulietta would never have another baby." Those words rang in my ears for months. I understood the literal translation of them, but at the time, I did not understand what they meant.

This is how Tina and I learned about life. This is how everyone in Murano learned that no matter what happens, life somehow goes on. This is how we *Muranesi* became strong, not just through our own experiences, but through those of others, people we cared about, as well as those we barely knew.

The Key to Paradise

When World War I started, Uncle Paolo was sent to fight in the Dolomite Mountains. In spite of the suffering he endured, he fell in love with the natural beauty of the area. In 1949, the year I was born, when his mirror company yielded some profits, he returned to the area and bought a beautiful Italian Villa in the little ghost town of Alano Di Piave.

Mama described to us how Uncle Paolo, with the enthusiasm of a child, refurbished the first two floors. He left the third floor empty to be completed at a later time. Uncle's wife, Aunt Lora, did not share the same zeal for the mountain, or for life in general. All she wanted to do was stay home and send her "poor husband" to the movies by himself with a piece of chocolate.

Disheartened, one day Uncle Paolo made a solo trip to his villa. He closed all the green shutters, locked the back and the front doors, chained the front gate with a double twist of heavy steel, and vowed never to return to his mountain house again, until. . . .

One Easter, as usual, Uncle Paolo, Aunt Lora and our other relatives came to our house to celebrate. The day was warm and the sky limpid. Wisteria fragrances filled the air. With a radiant smile on our faces, my siblings and I walked to church where we all sang with ardor to celebrate the resurrection of Jesus Christ. We girls felt proud in our pastel outfits, our Cloroxed white socks and white shoes. My sisters and I thought we looked regal wearing the white gloves Mama and Aunt Susi had used when they were young.

As I sat in church, I thought about the cookies my siblings, cousins and I were going to dip in the hot cocoa at Aunt Susi's house after Mass. I couldn't wait to eat the tantalizing chocolate eggs wrapped in shiny, colorful papers that Mama placed in the green dish on top of our credenza.

For Easter dinner, Gelmina and Mama cooked lasagna with homemade pasta and *besciamella* sauce. They braised the lamb Papa had brought home during the winter. The one we had kept in the laundry room at night and out on the terrace during the day and had fed with the bottle Mama had fed us with as well. The lamb we thought Papa had taken to Gelmina's family farm in the country a week before Easter, so that it could graze in the fields and enjoy freedom and fresh grass.

At one o'clock after everyone arrived at our house, Mama and Gelmina passed the serving dishes around the table. Amidst the ah-h-hs, the m-m-ms the *mamma mias,* and this is so good, Uncle Paolo interrupted us. Looking at my younger sister Giuliana's pale, gaunt cheeks, he said, "Teresa, Giuliana looks so pale! Is she still not well?"

Mama floundered for a few minutes before she answered.

"Uncle Paolo," she said, "the doctor said she should go to the mountains."

Mama lowered her eyes as if it were her fault that Giuliana had been sick with pneumonia.

Uncle Paolo seemed surprised. He looked at Mama's venerable countenance as he tried to grasp the simple words she had uttered.

"Teresa," he said, a sparkle in his eyes. "Tomorrow, I'll bring you the key to my villa in Alano di Piave. Take the children this summer and stay as long as you want."

His voice trembled. His eyes became a bit misty. Pride showed on his face for having thought of such a brilliant idea all on his own. He looked at her, and we all knew that he wished he had a wife like Mama and six children sitting around his kitchen table every day, and every holiday.

Uncle Paolo might as well have been Saint Peter handing the Key of Paradise to Mama, as one afternoon, a week after our arrival in the small town of Alano di Piave, as we stood in awe on the ridge of the valley in the back of Uncle's villa, Mama said, "Paradise must look like this. God is all around us."

To which, laughing, Gelmina added, "Where are the people? Signora Teresa, I think we can walk around town in our nightgowns. Nothing but ghosts in this town."

I wondered what Gelmina had meant when she said "nothing but ghosts" because on our very first day in Alano di Piave, we had met all of the inhabitants who lived in close proximity to Uncle's villa.

Emilia, the fruit vendor, a middle-aged woman, borderline cantankerous, lived in the back of the small store with her elderly father.

The grocery store owner, Dorina, with her toothless smile, her curly red hair springing from her head like the spikes of a porcupine, looking more like an elf than a human being, sat all day behind the counter. She had converted the front room of her house into a store. Day or night, any time you entered the store, her eighteen month old little giant, who had rosy puffy cheeks and reddish baby-fine hair, sat in the high chair that her husband had made for him out of pine wood. His little mouth opened as Dorina spoon-fed mashed potatoes, pureed vegetables, and homemade applesauce down his throat. She must have enjoyed feeding the baby because she just kept stuffing food in his mouth until the last tiny speck of food was gone from his plate. At times, we caught her singing him a mountain song, or talking to him as if he were a grown person.

The butcher, a heavy-set man in his mid-forties with white hair, a husky voice and an extra pound of salami or two around his middle, stood behind a massive counter. His demeanor was quite a contrast to his delicate, frail wife who, standing next to him, just reached his armpits. They lived with their three girls in a small, two-story house adjacent to his shop.

Antonina and Carlino resided in the big, yellow four-story villa next to our Uncle's, with their mother, grandmother and father, a most influential man. He was the director of the bank in a nearby town, and one of the few men left in town.

Uncle Paolo's villa was situated behind the main street, its main entrance by a *vicolo* paved with round rocks of different sizes and colors. The rocks, embedded in the street dirt, were contoured with moss. Within a few feet of Uncle's villa, an octagonal marble fountain, with red fish in it, stood in the center of a small square. From that center point, one could take a few steps to the café where the proprietor, Signor Ligio, sat outside smoking himself to death waiting for his few customers. Like his faithful mastiff dog, he growled and barked orders at his wife whose feet never touched the floor for fear of annoying her husband. She bore it all with a faint smile meant to mask the humiliation and ill treatment she received from him daily.

Between the fountain and the church, on each side of the only asphalted street, a few houses rolled one next to the other. In the center, on the left side of the road, as you walked uphill toward the church, a huge villa, a castle prototype—with two small towers and a black iron fence—stood as an anachronism in perennial silence.

"A *nera* lives there with a local man and their mulatto daughter," the butcher's three girls whispered the first time we walked by the castle.

Every year, come spring, all of the men in town left for a foreign country to earn money so that their families could survive during the winter months. They went to Austria, Switzerland, Germany, or wherever they could find work, leaving their loved ones and "their ghosts" behind.

In fact, Mama and Gelmina observed that the women acted and talked to their children as though their husbands were right there by their sides.

"Boys, come here. Your father wants you in bed by nine. Do you hear me?" Signora Paola from across the fountain reminded her two little boys.

During those early months in Alano di Piave, our family experienced a bit of paradise. We roamed about the countryside, unaffected by boundaries. We meandered up and down the gentle hills, and drank the pure fresh water that streamed in rivulets down the mountains towards the valley and into the large, rocky river where we often dipped our feet. We ate cherries, pears and plums off Uncle's trees, and grapes from the vines in back of the villa. We swished down the valley's green carpet all piled up in a toboggan, laughing and screaming from excitement. As we explored the mountainside, at times with our new-found friends, at times with Mama and Gelmina, we picked wild flowers, berries, hazelnuts and mushrooms. We walked through the thick forests in a single line, pretending to be explorers.

Often, Antonio, my oldest brother, yelled at us from the beginning of the line.

"Watch out, there is a hand-grenade on your right. Do not step on it."

From Uncle Paolo's kindness, we experienced a bit of paradise and a freedom we did not have, even on the small, safe island of Murano. Albeit, a paradise in which the sad events of World War I were still rooted within the birch trees, the moss, the rocks of the Dolomites. Pathways were paved with stones the soldiers had placed, one next to the other, just like the Romans had done many centuries before, to prevent their artilleries from sinking into the muddy land.

Uncle Paolo had spent a lot of time in the trenches fighting against the Austrians and the Central Powers. He knitted socks, scarves, and gloves for himself and for his friends so as not to freeze to death during the winter months when the temperature dropped below zero. Even when the trenches became long, mud puddles, he moved his needle in and out of the woolen loops from under his cape, trying to keep his work dry from the incessant rain.

We had found a Paradise where Hell had been.

When Uncle Paolo came over to our house with Aunt Lora for lunch during the holidays, he, like Uncle Ruggero, Mama's brother, who fought during World War II, recollected events about the war. They did not talk about it with regrets, or with hatred, or with horror, but with almost a sense of longing, of nostalgia for the friendships they formed in spite of the many atrocities they witnessed, for the intangible fabric they wove out of the fear of never coming back home.

A fabric tainted with blood-stains.

Uncle Paolo talked about the strength the soldiers gave each other as they squatted in the damp trenches for days, months, crying, laughing, singing, freezing almost to death. When a blanket of fog seemed to engulf the world around them, they stood still. They opened their eyes wide, trying to discern the gentle slopes of the Dolomites, the thick forest, the nearby birch trees. Cradled within the embrace of a faceless universe, they listened to the mute earth, speechless from so much sorrow. Wishing they were at home with their families, they found solace only in the touch of a hand, and the accidental brushing of their friends' shoulders. Immobile, their thoughts frozen, they longed for peace. As they leaned against the muddy walls of the trenches, waiting, they held their wounded friends and the dead ones.

In spite of the sorrow that surrounded them, they wove a mighty, strong fabric, which they pieced together with the small miracles that burst forth in the most implausible conditions.

They drew strength from spectacular sunsets, from the chirping of the wild birds awaking them at the first sight of dawn, from delicate spring flowers, from the multicolor leaves of fall, and from a mutual love for their country and families. When the trees changed and the myriad colors of fall appeared, when Uncle sank his mountain boots in the spongy blanket of multicolored dry leaves, palliating even if for a few precious moments the color of the war, his heart, and that of his fellow soldiers felt looped into nature's magical realm.

As we gathered around the table eating our Easter dinner, Uncle Paolo said, "During the war, thinking about my mama in church praying with her friends gave me strength and courage."

Aunt Claretta said that during World War I, her mama and the ladies in Murano sat in the huge multipurpose room by the church and paired two by two. One lady held an old woolen garment, unraveling it, while the other gathered it with circular movements in one huge ball. Bundled up in their winter coats in the icy multipurpose room, they warmed each other with small anecdotes or tales about their sons. They moved their mouths at the same time, often listening only to their own fears and anxiety. As they spilled out their sorrows, their words froze in midair.

"Here, Signora Anna," one lady said to grandmother. "Here is another wool ball for your son. God bless him and all of our children in those trenches."

"The war," said another lady with a sigh, "the war only kills. And what does it accomplish? Nothing but destruction."

"God bless our young men," lamented another one. "I wonder what they are doing at this moment. I wonder if they have plenty of food to eat."

"Did anyone hear any news?"

"Rosa, did you receive a letter? Yesterday, the mailman said you received a letter," Lina said.

Rosa took out a soiled piece of paper from her pocket and began to unfold it while a faint smile sat on her lips.

"*Si, Si*, Lina," replied Rosa. "My Son Lio wrote me a very short letter. He said he was hungry and cold. He said not to worry. He said. . . he can't wait to come home and eat my *pasticcio di lasagna*."

"Did you hear that the milkman's son died?"

"What? Oh no. Oh no. What happened?"

"Eleonora said her mother walks around with the picture of her son on her breast and cries, cries. . . ."

Their gatherings were more than just the assemblage of wool bundles. The gatherings were a tacit symbol of assent, of approval, of comfort for circumstances they had no control over and could only pray about with all of their hearts.

Aunt Claretta said her mother had a real sense of duty for her country. During the war, she often declared in a solemn tone, bending her neck backward the way she often did when she approved of something, "When your country calls you, your other loves must remain silent."

During our Easter luncheons, a soft smile on his face, cognizant of amusing us, sure to be teaching us a lesson, Uncle Paolo revealed how he became the expert in the art of knitting, and crocheting, and how during the war he taught knitting to the other soldiers.

Many years before the war, around the holidays, when he complained that he wanted to surprise his sisters with a gift but had no money, his Mama showed Uncle Paolo how to knit. A few days before the sixth of December, Saint Nicolò day, after everyone had gone to bed, Uncle Paolo and his mother stayed up till late. Grandmother taught him how to make a scarf and a hat with the wool from an old sweater she had unraveled for him. That skill, so simple and innocent, had became instrumental in keeping him and some of the other young Italian soldiers warm when the temperature dropped below zero, or when the loose dirt of summer changed into a film of thin ice as the trenches became their own ice boxes. In spite of the hardships Uncle Paolo suffered, he grew to love the gentle hills of the Dolomites, the forest, and the large burbling rivulets that scurried throughout the valley in spring and summer.

Uncle Paolo's Villa

Iremember the first time we arrived at Uncle Paolo's villa. At the beginning of summer, early in the morning, our whole family walked to the boat station, transferred to the train station, and on to the bus station. We lugged our many suitcases filled with sheets, kitchen and bath towels, summer clothes, and whatever else Mama and Gelmina thought to pack.

At twelve o'clock, we arrived at the small, empty square in Alano di Piave. Famished, we stepped out of the bus and stood like aliens near the octagonal marble fountain. In silent reverence, Papa took a deep breath, sniffing the scent of pasta coming from the open door of the café. Not sure which direction to take, we scanned the empty *piazza*, the tall dark green pines, the walnuts, and the chestnut trees. They stood against the bright, blue sky tinted only by an occasional patch of faint, white clouds. The jagged lines of the hills Uncle Paolo had described loomed in the distance. We gazed at the lofty mountains, and at the swallow that flew in and out of the cafe's eaves.

"This is Cezanne!" Papa said. "Teresa, did we bring my colors and my brushes?" Turning all the way around, Papa searched for a three-story building surrounded by a brick wall coated with cement specks on the outside and contoured all around with black steel poles, eight inches apart, curved at the top with a twirl like the horns of a ram.

"I think we need to walk in that direction," Papa said, stepping away from the fountain.

"This way," he uttered with enthusiasm as he snapped his fingers with a twist of his hand.

Each of us picked up our luggage and followed behind up the hill.

Papa stopped at the villa's gate. With elbows on the wall and standing on our toes, we gathered together to peer at a huge front yard, which at one time must have been a beautiful European Garden. By now the garden had metamorphosed into masses of weeds and overgrown bushes. While Papa tried to unlock the gate, we admired the four, gigantic trees facing the front façade of the house.

At the brown double door, Mama stopped and turned the key in the rusted lock. She pushed the door inward with Gelmina's and Papa's help and poked her head in.

"Stop. Do not come in," Mama ordered while she scanned the huge entrance hall.

"Gabri, Antonio, gather the suitcases and sit on them till we clean a bit."

Her words were lost in the wind. Instead of sitting, we wandered all over the grounds. We ran back into the small *piazza*, walked to the *fontana*, watched two of the butcher's daughters who had come out of their house to see who had arrived on the twelve o'clock bus.

The younger of the two girls took a piece of her chewing-gum out of her mouth and handed it to her elder sister, who in turn, put it in her own mouth. I stared at the exchange as I thought about Mama who always said not to drink out of other people's glasses, wishing I could have a small piece of gum myself.

Before I could think, *Santa Madre!* the elder of the two girls approached me and handed me a piece of that same gum. Embarrassed, I placed it in my mouth as she said in her country dialect, *"Che nome ga veiu tosate?"* "What are your names, girls?"

We had a grand time at Uncle Paolo's villa. Mama and Gelmina cleaned Uncle's villa with as much strength as they cleaned our house in the springtime when the priest came to bless it. Papa, who came on weekends, bought Mama live rabbits and chickens so that Giuliana could drink a fresh raw egg each morning and become strong again. So that Gelmina could mix egg yolks with a few tablespoons of sugar till they turned to a creamy pale yellow, and feed it to us as a treat on rainy afternoons. That first summer, Giuliana regained her rosy cheeks and her health.

Poor Uncle! He had bought the villa because he hoped to have a big family like Papa. God gave Papa children, but not money. He gave Uncle

Paolo money, but not children. Papa shared us with Uncle Paolo, and in exchange, Uncle shared his beautiful, old villa with Papa for many years.

Delectable Goods

When Tina and I were together, time went by fast. As we sat on the cemetery's stone steps, we talked about boys, about school, about homework, about our studying in the bathroom, the only place in our houses where we both could have peace and quiet. There, we could read without having to listen to the buzzing and humming of family members, of friends who without any prior notice stopped by our houses, unannounced, even at eleven o'clock at night.

We laughed at the expression "peace and quiet" as Tina was quick to point out that peace reigned in the bathroom only until someone cranked at the pewter handle with vehemence. The subsequent desperate poundings on the wooden door and loud impatient utterances, "*Verzi, verzi, presto, verzi,*" alerted us to the urgency of the call.

The muffled voices of occasional passersby, the sounds of small insects and other creatures dwelling in the surrounding field, the dark area lit only by the brilliant moon, felt great. It felt more than great to be talking to my best friend. Away from the scrutiny of people and the sanctions of adults, with no one reading our facial expressions and minds, I could be myself. It was grand to sit outside the cemetery entrance, the night cold autumn wind making our cheeks, knees, hands and legs feel like ice.

Sometimes, we just sat in silence.

As our eyes became acclimated to the dark, we looked at the shiny constellations that spread unabashed in the dark cloth of night. We pointed at Cassiopeia, Big Bear and Little Bear.

"Look, Big Bear," I whispered, and then became silent again.

In our minds, we each chose the brightest star to be our very own. We stared at the pulsing constellations for long intervals in peaceful, silent reverence and often lingered there later than we were allowed to be out.

One particular night, when we realized that it was already eight p.m., I jumped up from the steps as I threw Tina her shoes. I slipped mine on without bothering to tie them. I ran down the muddy, unpaved narrow path and crossed the field, while Tina shouted something to me about meeting again the next day.

The streets were deserted. Everyone was at home having dinner. I ran as fast as I could. I saw no one untill I crossed *Campo San Bernardo*. In the far distance, a tall figure turned the corner, but I did not recognize who it was.

I heard voices coming from the dark entrance of one of the four-story buildings. I twisted my head and body in all directions to make sure no one was following me. Few shutters on the façade of the buildings were still open. My eyes rose to observe the comforting lights diffusing in the open air in the forms of geometrical shadows. I scanned the *campo* for cats.

I was afraid of cats. The occasional "meow" coming from under the houses always frightened me. If I spied a cat approaching with his slinky movements, crossing or stopping in the middle of the *fondamenta*, I changed my route and took the scenic tour home even if it was late. I had a skittish attitude towards cats even if my papa told me that cats were important because they hunted the mice in the lagoon and surrounding islands. I understood what Papa said, but I still feared cats. They gave me horrible nightmares, and made me sweat as if I had a high fever and the shakes. Cats frightened me the same way as when I dreamed about being buried alive.

I thought of stopping for a few seconds to rest but decided against it since I knew Mama would be pacing from the table to the kitchen window looking for me. As I ran, I prepared myself to answer Mama's hundred questions. When I reached *Calle Conterie*, I sighed with relief, "I'm almost home."

The moment I stepped into the kitchen, Mama said, "Why did you come home so late. Didn't you notice the dark outside? Someone saw you at the *Ponte Lungo* with Tina earlier. Where did you go? Not to the cemetery, I hope."

I knew it was no use to lie.

Sheepishly, I sat in my empty place between my younger sister Margherita and my brother Pietro, and with a glance of silent understanding, I implored Papa to intercede.

"*Bambina*, you know your mama worries," Papa said in his reassuring tone, before I found my voice.

"Tomorrow, come home a little earlier so that we can all be together. I was just talking about your grandfather. Isn't it true, Mama?"

Papa turned towards Mama.

Mama knew he did not want a scene at the dinner table. Resigned, Mama nodded her head with a sigh. She shook her head and sat down next to Papa and Gelmina. Papa began to talk about his father. I knew that Mama was thinking of how they perceived life in a different way, of how nothing fazed Papa. Or at least, it appeared that nothing fazed him. In a way, it was good that his personality differed from Mama. With his affability, he helped alleviate her worries. Papa was always there for Mama, to reassure her with his own internal spirituality.

Papa trusted God and His entourage, the Virgin Mary, and all of the Saints, especially Saint Nicolò, to provide and attend to our needs implicitly. Father Matteo had said to Mama in the fancy way he used when he wanted to impress his parishioners, that Papa's liminal point of his ideology could not be discerned. He said that for Papa, the celestial and the terrestrial blended together in harmony. For Papa, one could not exist without the other.

Mama explained to us that it was a fancy way to say that Papa's faith was like a perfectly delicious cake: you could not distinguish the ingredients after it was baked, even though they were all there on the inside. Of course, Mama was a strong believer as well, but she did not have a blind trust as Papa did. She trusted that God would help us, but she worried herself silly in the process. That was the difference. Papa knew that God worried for him.

Sometimes, Mama thought Papa was not real. That is what I thought of him, too. He made up his own universe. Almost an ethereal being, his spirit floated and danced within his dreams in the stratosphere. He hummed his opera pieces, sang his favorite romantic ballads in his *baritono* voice, entertained us with his magic tricks, and performed good, sincere deeds to people in need.

On occasion, Mama told us that she would not have made it without Papa. She said that she would not have liked to have a husband who went out every night with his friends instead of coming home as Papa did. Or a tyrant like her friend's husband who counted every penny she spent. Or one with a mistress who bought his wife a new piece of silver to keep her happy with each new love affair.

Instead, Papa came home with small packages full of peanuts or chestnuts or currants for all of us to celebrate with.

I think Mama was pleased with Papa because one time she said to me that he had a good character and a deep sense of right and wrong. He was a good husband and father. A good person. Of course, she would have liked to have had a little more money, but money, as important as it was, was not one of Papa's priorities. As scarce as money had been, I could read in Mama's eyes that she still was happy she married Papa.

With Papa dreaming so much, I think the mere thought of having money gave him even more pleasure than possessing it. Of course, we knew he wanted money. He said so one night during dinner when Gabri asked for some money to buy her school books. Papa said that money was a necessary evil, and that we needed it to survive. From that simple explanation, we understood that he did not have the money to give Gabri for her books.

"*Bambini,*" he said with solemnity as if he were revealing the mystery of life and death, "Money does not open the door to Paradise. That is one place where you cannot buy a ticket to go in. Isn't it true, Mama?"

I noticed Mama's facial muscles relax. Her lips parted as a faint smile rose on her face. She folded her arms on her lap and crossed her legs.

"Teresa, wasn't my father an excellent cook?"

Papa's question startled Mama.

She nodded. Papa said that when he was young, at the twelfth gong of the clock tower, he and his six siblings ran home hoping to find some tomato sauce to dip in the yellow *polenta.*

"*Bambini,* you are so lucky," Papa said. "When young, I waited all morning for the gong while my stomach growled, so I could run home before the tomato sauce in my Papa's pot was gone."

"Mama! Mmmm, it was so tasty!" Papa closed his eyelids for an instant, lifted his chin, and even tried to inhale the imaginary scent of his father's tomato sauce. Mama thought that perhaps Papa's craving for his father's food stemmed from nostalgia of a time long gone. Or from the memories of how his father celebrated when he made *polenta* cookies, *polenta* pudding, *polenta* soup during The Depression when there was nothing else to eat.

Papa painted a colorful picture of his father by the stove stirring his famous sauce and the *polenta*. He draped his narrative with emphatic gestures as he explained how his father dipped his wooden spoon with ceremonious flair, holding it with his fingertips as he lifted his forearm and head forward. He placed the tip of the spoon in his mouth and sipped the few drops of dark, red thick tomato paste with gusto. Papa bragged that his father had a penchant for cooking, and talked about all of the wonderful dishes he made "out of nothing."

As Papa talked, we looked at Mama. "It's true," she whispered, shaking her head. "His father was a good cook, but they had truly nothing. His family had nothing to eat, nothing, nothing."

To conceal embarrassment, Margherita and Pietro chortled as they blushed, and while a tear spurted from my eye, Antonio, my eldest brother, motioned to Margherita and Pietro to keep quiet and to listen to what Papa was saying.

Every chance he got, Papa described his father's delectable food. We even tasted some of it when Mama, on occasion, agreed to prepare the cookies Papa's father used to make, albeit, adding generous amounts of butter, pine nuts and raisins which were missing in grandfather's.

On those occasions, Papa put one cookie in his mouth, slowly chewing, making sure he extracted the buttery flavor from it. He rubbed his tongue against his palate and closed his eyes to appreciate the cookie even more. With the satisfied look of a chef who had just tasted his new recipe, he proclaimed, "Ohh. . .Teresa, this cookie is so good! Just like father's."

"Ah, this man," Mama would say. "What am I going to do with this man."

Perhaps Papa was like his father, acting with us children like his own father must have done with Papa and his siblings so that, they would not feel the dearth of what people called the "necessities of life." That is why

Papa filled his and our lives with small pleasures. Via the everyday rituals, the celebrations, the small lessons of love, he passed on to us the true essence of life.

Papa's Sixtieth Birthday

On Papa's sixtieth birthday, I cried all day. I had been careful not to let Papa see me crying. I did not want him to know that I thought he was too old. I wanted a Papa like Tina's, young, with a boy-like physique, who bounced and strutted all over the *fondamenta* as if he were on parade. A Papa who could live for a long time way past my childhood, one who would be there when I got married and one who would have the opportunity to play with my children.

During school, on Papa's birthday, my accounting instructor asked me if I had been crying. And Signora Maria, the after-school tutor, a friend of the family who helped me, my five siblings, and most of the children in Murano with our homework, said holding my hand, "Anna. . .look, do not worry about your Papa. You'll see how long he is going to live."

"Nico is so *pacifico*," she whispered as she pushed my bangs away from my forehead.

Signora Maria had said "*pacifico*" just like the Pacific Ocean. Papa was calm, his personality like the Pacific Ocean during one of its peaceful moods.

Mama smiled when I said that I worried about Papa's dying and held me tight for a moment.

"Do not worry, Anna," she said as she kissed the top of my head. "Your Papa is going to live for a long time." Mama paused as if in search for something more to say.

"Just watch your Papa tonight," she added. "See how happy he is." She said that as if happiness and longevity were synonymous with one another, as if being happy meant living a longer life.

Perhaps my fears of death stemmed from Father Matteo's sermon. A few days before Papa's birthday, I had gone with my friend Tina to the church to listen to Father Matteo's Bible stories. He had told us about people of long ago. He said that when the archeologists unearthed their skeletons, the arms had been found clutching their skulls in desperation. It meant people had been buried alive.

Father Matteo's vivid gesticulations, the selection of well-chosen words, the mysterious diction in his voice, the expression in his eyes, the beads of sweat lined across his forehead spooked me and made the characters in the story come alive even if they had been dead for centuries.

I dug my fingernails into Tina's hand. Afterward, even though Tina and I discussed how terrible it would be to be buried alive, I dreamed about dead people whose hands clutched their skulls.

On Papa's birthday, I awoke at dawn from a muffled cry of what I imagined to be a baby locked up in a coffin. With my body and mind paralyzed with fear as if I had seen a rattlesnake, I lay in bed soaked in sweat. I listened for any unusual sounds and felt claustrophobic. Unable to move one single inch of my limbs, I turned my gaze towards the windows and noticed the faint rays of morning light coming through the chinks of the closed, green shutters. On the bed adjacent to mine, Margherita slept peacefully, pillow on her chest, hugging it as if it were a small baby.

I'm home! I'm in my bedroom, I thought, as I breathed a sigh of relief. I moved my head, looked at Gabri's distorted face, mouth agape, white saliva trailing down her chin, nose buried in the soft, woolen pillow. I heard Gelmina snoring in the bed next to Gabri, but I still could not breathe with ease.

Immobile, while in bed, I shuddered at the thought of being buried alive, of being all locked up in a satin padded coffin without any hope of being rescued.

As I forced myself to think of something else, I heard Antonio and Pietro's voices in the kitchen sing Happy Birthday to Papa, and my eyes filled with tears.

High Tide

Every year come fall, the entire Murano population watched for any turn in weather which might cause the tide to overflow. At the slightest inkling of a change, they observed the canal water crashing with impetus against the brick walls of the century-old houses. Filled with espresso coffee, they pressed their noses against the glass windows for most of the night, their bulging eyes, peering through the darkness.

When we thought the voracious tide might gulp down our small island, my siblings and I listened for Papa's instructions.

"I don't like it," Papa uttered as he scanned the sky. "I don't like it at all."

He tapped at his nose to let us know that he smelled something in the air; something that would give everyone much to do throughout the evening and into the night. Papa pointed his finger at the sky to warn us that the moon, majestic as a queen, was working overtime to suck the water from its comfortable bed. Like a doting mother, the moon let her child out of its constraints and watched the child crawl and swish back and forth on the streets, pestering everyone.

Papa opened the balcony door of our apartment and stepped out for a moment, chin tilted towards the sky as if he were expecting a warning, or an announcement from above. He sniffed the air, stared at the full moon, and tested the direction of the wind with his finger.

"The moon, mistress of the tides, tyrant of the sea," Papa muttered under his breath, a wondrous inflection in his voice.

"Watch your friends and enemies alike," he warned us.

In awe of nature, Papa fully imbued himself with its scent. Like a hawk, he kept a watchful eye on it.

During the day, when thunder and lightning struck as a prelude to a thunderstorm, people uttered, "Listen. Listen. . .Today Saint Peter is going to wash his wine-barrels."

People were very much in tune with nature, to her tricks, to her capricious moods. If the tide did not ebb but remained steady throughout the day, the unheard sound of a nonexistent siren went off, and everyone did their part in helping their stranded families and friends alike.

"High tide tonight," they alerted each other as they passed on the streets, or even from the other side of the canal.

Everyone knew what needed to be done.

Signora Rosa, a widow, who lived by herself on the ground floor of the same apartment building we did, cemented a thirty inch wood plank to her front door to stop the flow of salty water from entering her house and ruining her Venetian marble floor and her furniture. In her subtle way, she let us know she did not want any help. It was her way to assert her independence a little longer.

When Signora Rosa finished her carpentry job, she called on the first passerby, a young man.

"*Giovanotto, Giovanotto*, please can you help me," she whispered so that no one in the apartment building could hear her. As she placed her gnarled fingers in the young man's palm, she raised her wool pleated skirt—the one she always wore to cement the door. She lifted one leg and then the other over the windowsill of her kitchen window. Reciting her medical text, she explained to the young man about the incapacitating effect arthritis had on her body. The proud Signora Rosa wanted him to understand that arthritis crippled her, not old age.

At the first sign of high tide, Signor Gianni, the grocery store's owner, called my siblings and me to lift the big sacks of potatoes, rice, flour and pasta piled one next to the other on the floor. As he kept an eye on us to make sure we did not spill the contents, he waited on his customers.

"Signora Alice, do you see how helpful these children are?" he said as he winked. "For sure they earned a big licorice today."

Signora Alice twisted her body toward us, careful not to lose her place in the non-existent line.

"*Bravi, bambini. . .bravi,*" she said with a flaring voice, turning to Signor Gianni as if he needed an answer to his remark.

Signora Alice added with nonchalance in her Venetian dialect, "*Eh bè,* they know we all need to help. Oh, yes, they are good children. Their grandmother. . .a good woman. And, the mother, too. *Brava gente. Si, brava gente.*"

We children glanced at each other with smiling eyes as we felt proud. Our main thoughts on the licorice we were going to stick in the half lemon that Signor Giorgio, the fruit-vendor, would give us after we helped him, as well.

When the water swelled and rose just a few centimeters above the paved *fondamenta,* adults and children alike wore high rubber boots. They walked against the walls of the shops and houses, afraid to mistake the streets with the canal and to fall into the deep, dark green pool of water. The small shops, whose floors had been elevated over the years to a higher plateau so as to prevent the water from entering, put up walking paths made of elevated large wooden planks so that people could still purchase their daily necessities without getting their feet wet.

At a sign of high tide, Papa reminded my brother, "Antonio, take out the high rubber boots and the yellow plastic hood. You want your hands free to hold on to the bridge-rails in case you have to help someone to safety."

Antonio placed the supplies by the front door, ready to go and lift Great Aunt Nice and Aunt Susi's furniture off the floor before the flood took it for a stroll around the rooms of their house.

At times, the tide crept up slowly but stopped rising just before it reached the top of the *fondamenta.* On those occasions, people breathed a sigh of relief and resumed their daily routine as though nothing had happened.

One day, at six a.m., the pounding on the bathroom door woke me up.

"Open up. . .Open up," I heard Gabri shouting. "I have to go to work. We have an order to fill. Open. Mama! I'm in a hurry. Mama, tell Margherita to come out of the bathroom."

"Quiet, Gabri," Mama said. "It is only six o'clock. You are going to wake up all of the neighbors."

"Tell Margherita to get out," Gabri said as she pounded on the bathroom door with continued vigor.

I was glad I had bathed the night before in the kitchen sink behind the screen by the stove, the only warm place in the house. I did not mind taking a sponge bath at one o'clock in the night after the last member of the family had gone to bed, as I did not want to bathe in the freezing bathroom. Nor did I want to fight the morning crowd.

I opened my eyes, but could not see anything. The shutters were closed. It was still dark outside. I reached for the lamp switch on the side table but the light did not work. I got up and walked towards the closed door.

I rubbed my eyes, walked into the kitchen, and kissed Mama and Gelmina who had been up since five. Mama said that the early morning hours were the best time of the day. In the profound silence of dawn she could think in peace without any interruptions.

As in a ritual, each morning Mama washed the kitchen floor, ironed our clothes and uniforms. Gelmina lit the stove and shined our shoes.

"*Acqua alta. Acqua alta gavemo,*" someone shouted from the street.

I walked by the window to see if the sky was clear. I looked through the naked wisteria branches on the iron net wall that surrounded Signora Rosina's apartment.

"High tide. We are going to have high tide," I heard a worker's voice shout.

"*Acqua alta, Mama,*" I said.

"*Eh, si,*" Mama sighed, "It's the season."

I looked up at Mama. I knew what Mama meant when she said, "It's the season for high tide." A new season was starting again. In fact, you could feel it, not only enveloping your body, but swallowing its core as well.

The high tide signaled that winter was piercing through fall. It meant that a hard winter lay ahead full of surprises with utterly uncomfortable dark, gloomy days and freezing starry nights. It meant more work for Mama and Gelmina, wet garments spread on the kitchen table and chairs before we went to bed at night, hoping that in the morning everything would be dry from the warmth of the stove. For Mama and Aunt Susi, it meant more sewing, taking apart, cutting, and reassembling to a different size, the old, hand me down wool coats some adult members of the family gave to Mama for us.

Papa entered the kitchen, humming the chorus from Verdi's opera, La Traviata. He always came in cheerful, with his ubiquitous *gioia di vivere* in his heart, his body swaying. He walked towards Mama and kissed her on the forehead.

"Hi, how are you this morning, Gelmina?" Papa said, turning to Gelmina.

Papa, Mama, Gelmina, Gabri, Antonio, Margherita and I sat around the kitchen table eating our breakfast while the two youngest siblings were still asleep. With the electricity off, the kitchen glowed from the dim light of a candle in the center of the table.

I sipped the last drop of tepid milk and coffee. Slouching in my chair, I folded my arms and waited for Papa, Gabri and Antonio to leave, so I could wash my face, brush my teeth, and go to school. I should have studied and reviewed my math assignment, the word-problems. But there was no point in doing that because I did not understand word-problems.

My eyes rested for a moment on Papa's clay castle on top of the credenza. Next to it, his canvas, still without a frame, leaned against the wall.

Papa had stroked the canvas with much passion night after night during the litigation with Uncle Nano for the division of the factory's goods. He painted it when things became tense and he needed a distraction to ease the profound sadness he felt. He had depicted a colorful bouquet of fresh flowers in a transparent glass vase, which he himself had engraved. Humming his favorite tunes, he filled his canvas with short, decisive strokes. Every night, after Mama cleared the table, he took out the palette, a few brushes and the oil colors which he squeezed to the last drop to make them last longer. He stroked on his canvas with pride, losing himself in the fervor of his task.

"Van Gogh-like," Papa said after he finished his work of art and stepped back to admire his *natura morta*.

"Teresa, where should we put my still life?"

Mama looked around at the walls already crowded with some of the country scenes Papa had painted during the summer out in the fields adjacent to Uncle Paolo's villa. Mama scanned the cluttered top of the *credenza.* She stepped on a chair, stretched her arm as far as she could and pushed the multicolored Venetian glass clown to the far side. She grabbed the canvas from Papa's hands, placed it next to the clay castle, leaned it against the wall and stepped down. She walked back as far as she could, beside Papa.

"Nico," Mama said, "I like it."

Papa melted with pride.

When Papa left the room, Mama told Gelmina that at first she had not liked the combination of colors he used for the *sottofondo.* Too loud, she thought. But, from afar, from the top of the *credenza*, the effect of the warm beige, orange and dark brown as a *sottofondo* to the red, orange and white bouquet, was rather pleasing to the eye.

The deafening sound of thunder, and the fiery lightning erupted through the shutters of our kitchen window, startling everyone.

"Did you see that lightning?" Papa uttered in amazement. "It fell nearby. The power of nature. Oh yes, what a fantastic force." Then he added, "We need to go."

Mama did not want Papa to go to the factory because he had been sick with bronchitis and fever, and the doctor had given her strict orders to keep him home for a few more days.

Papa protested.

He complained that he felt fine, that he did not have a fever, and that his bronchitis would improve with a few treatments of *fumenti*, Papa's panacea for colds. He swore his "scientific" treatment opened his nasal passages. *Fumenti* consisted of one large bowl of hot boiling water with a few drops of liquid menthol, the huge, white towel with Mama's embroidered initials, and Papa's head buried under it like a turtle, breathing the fumes through his nose until the water stopped steaming.

A few times a day, as well, Mama placed a compress of a creamy mixture of wheat wrapped in a large handkerchief on Papa's congested chest. She set the mixture on top of his wool undershirt so his skin would not burn. Since the doctor, according to Papa, did not know what he was talking about, Papa cured all of his and our malaises with vegetable soup or a shot of brandy in a bowl of piping hot milk right before we went to sleep.

Mama and Papa argued in the midst of the thunder and lightning. Papa insisted on going out. Mama refused to let him go.

"Bambini," Papa said, after he finished his breakfast, "if the wind does not subside, and the rain does not stop, we are in for it."

He paused for a second.

"Teresa," he said to Mama, "Do we have enough to eat? What are we having for lunch?"

"But, Nico," Mama replied, "you still have food in your mouth and you are already thinking about lunch? When young, you must have suffered much hunger."

"Why do you say that, Teresa? You know food is one of my pleasures in life. I do not ask for much, do I?"

Then Papa flirted with Mama in a way that made everyone laugh.

"Teresa, all I want today is boiled tongue with candied mustard. A few quails stuffed with sausages, topped with mushroom sauce the way only you can prepare. And a big plate of fresh spinach, *lessati*, with a sprinkle of olive oil and salt on it. "

As he pronounced the word *lessati*, Papa lifted his hand to chin level and joined the tips of his thumb and of his index finger to form a semicircle. He moved his hand from left to right in a gesture that implied excellence.

With smiling eyes, Papa turned his head around to see if everyone was amused by his humor.

Papa won the battle.

"Gabri, are you ready? Look, Mama, how wonderful Gabri is. She is ready for work."

"And Antonio, is he ready?"

Mama nodded. "He is in his bedroom."

"Good." Then turning to me, he said, "Anna, are you coming after school? What time should I expect you? We have a lot of work to do."

"Yes, Papa, I'll come after lunch."

After Papa, Gabri, and Antonio left, I put on my boots and my rain gear, gathered my books together and left to catch the boat for Venice.

I walked through *Calle Conterie,* and *Calle del Mistro* where the water had just begun to gush out of the gutters, invading the whole *calle.* I swished in the salty water as the rain storm spattered on all the surfaces.

The fierce force of the wind against the water brought it up to a higher level. I shielded myself with Papa's big black umbrella, but its skeleton reversed several times. Before I could say, *"Mamma mia,* I'm scared," the wind had pushed me against the wall.

You would think it was noontime from the amount of people walking about in the expanse of water, going to and from their glass factories, their small laboratories, their shops, trying to salvage all they could.

Friends shouted to each other. "Be careful and pay attention! Walk against the wall!"

"Hi, Toni. What a day!"

"Gigio, be careful. At your age, you should be home. Where are your children?" Gigio muttered something in response to the rhetorical utterances, which got lost in the labyrinth of rain.

People hurried to complete their tasks.

One hand on the wall, I slowly lumbered up to *Ponte Lungo,* holding on to the closed umbrella. Reluctant to move on, I stood for a moment at the bottom of the bridge, freezing, hoping to meet my friend Tina as every day, we traveled in the boat together. Once in Venice, we walked the first three blocks till Tina reached the gate of her school, The Professional Institute of Commerce.

Because of the rain, I did not wait for her.

As I walked, the shops and apartment buildings unfolded one next to the other in front of me. Great Aunt Nice and Aunt Susi's house appeared and disappeared like a flash before my eyes. I could not discern the people walking about. The roaring wind and the ceaseless rain fell like a glass beaded curtain in the tumultuous water. What ordinarily appeared to be the safest and most enchanting island, now was engulfed by two converging, roaring forces.

I stopped for a few minutes at the *pasticceria* and waited for the rain to subside before I moved ahead. I thought of Papa's old saying, "The Moon, mistress of the tide, tyrant of the sea."

I looked up, but could not see the moon as it hid behind the still, gray sky, perhaps, ashamed to be seen.

Soaked all the way through my rain gear, uncomfortable, wet and annoyed, I thought about the warmth I had felt earlier in Mama and Papa's kitchen when we sat around the table, talking by the glow of the green candle.

By the time I arrived at the *Colonna* — the first boat station if one came from Venice, but the last one for me who walked all the way from *San Donato* — the rain had stopped completely, but the sky was still clouded. As I walked, I listened to the swishing of my boots against the water. I heard people talking to each other about the weather and about the high-tide which was supposed to ebb just before I got out of school. I bid a few people *buon giorno*.

I had missed the seven-thirty boat, and the one after that. Judging by the number of people at the boat station, I assumed that the boats were not on time, either. I breathed a sigh of relief when I saw some of the regular crowd still there.

I smiled at Gabri's friend, Norma, who was biting into a green apple. Norma commuted every morning to Padova.

She was lucky. Her Papa and Mama did not have their own business, so they sent their children to the University.

Mama had said that Norma was very smart. When she said that, Mama lowered her eyes and began to embroider one of Gabri's kitchen towels for her dowry. I could see from Mama's demeanor that she would have liked Gabri to go to the university like Norma.

I vaguely remembered Mama telling me that one of Gabri's professors had come to the house after she completed the *Istituto of Economia Domestica*, and tried to convince Papa to let Gabri continue with her studies. The professor said that Gabri was very smart and capable of doing anything she set her mind to.

"Gabri is very talented," he said, "the best in her class."

He said that if Gabri remained in school, she could have taught *Economia Domestica* at their school. The professor presented a compelling speech, but. . . it was no use.

Mama knew Gabri was smart.

"I do not think Gabri is very happy helping your father. It would be better if she went to school," Mama had said to me, her voice quivering.

It was not to be.

Gabri was needed at Papa's factory. The family was more important. That was just how it was. She was going to be the secretary, even if Gabri did not like numbers and calculations. Nor business letters for that matter, and would have preferred concocting exotic delicate dishes. She would have been perfect teaching in a culinary school. Gelmina always said that Gabri could prepare and gulp down the food faster than Mama could place it on a serving dish, and could lick all of her ten fingers in the interim. Fueled by a much-spirited disposition, in the end Gabri's food metamorphosed into thousands of words.

Gabri wanted to be an *au pair*. She wanted to go to England.

"Papa, can I go to England," she asked.

"Teresa, wouldn't it be nice if Gabri could go to England? She could learn the language, then speak English to my customers," Papa said.

"Papa, can we buy a hotel near the train station? I hear that the *Frati Salesiani* want to sell theirs or to find a manager," Gabri announced one day.

"Teresa, wouldn't it be nice if we bought the hotel? Look, we have so many children, they all could help," Papa said.

"Oh, sure. And Gelmina and I would work even harder than we do right now."

"Papa, can I go to Africa to be a missionary? My friend is leaving for Cameroon in a few months. Can I go too, Papa, please, Papa, Papa, can I go, too?"

"Mama, what do you think?" Papa turned, so he could read in Mama's expression, first a profound sadness, then a clear determination to let things stand at their status quo. My resolute Mama believed that in unity there was strength, and in strength, survival.

I looked around to see if the boat was in sight. The wind had subsided, but my wet body made me shiver. I secured and fastened my soaked headscarf tighter. I did not want anyone to see my kinky hair. I hated curly hair. It made my face appear even more rounded. One thought gave me comfort, though. Today was Friday, and on Friday at one o'clock in the afternoon, Laura, my school friend, came over to my house to set my hair on the pink, plastic rollers Gelmina had given me for Christmas. Then I remembered I had to go to Papa's factory, so I made a mental note to tell Laura not to come.

I scanned the front of the boat station to see if my friends Davide and Aldo were there. Like all of my friends, they too, caught the seven thirty boat to Venice. I did not want Davide to see me. My face was probably purple from the cold, and one day on the bridge, Aldo had teased me that in winter my face looked like a small *salame*. I hated him saying that, especially in front of Davide.

Like the shifting tide, I took small steps, my body widening the gap between people. As I advanced toward the front of the station I heard Davide and Aldo laughing. I positioned myself behind a strata of people and peered at Davide through the cracks. I spied his yellow plastic coat and his brown rain boots. I felt a deep blush on my face and wished Tina was there. I tried to move back but could not. The small rectangular boat station, now crowded with commuters, was swaying with vehemence. A huge freight boat, and a private launch zooming from opposite directions, intersected a few feet away, causing the waves to splash against the station. My body oscillated. I moved a few steps sideways and bumped my neighbor's arm. I felt a firm grasping hand on my shoulder.

"*Scusi, Signorina* Anna," a man's voice said.

People fidgeted like a school of fish trapped in a net, looking for a way out. They complained about the weather, the inconvenience of the high-tide, the boat being late, and about the time they were wasting, waiting.

"You can never count on the boat to be on time," Signora Ada said aloud to no one in particular.

"As if we had nothing better to do, but to wait for the boat," she added looking right and left at a few concurring heads.

"What do the workers care? They are not in a hurry, are they? They get paid anyway, right?"

People chatted back and forth, overlapping their conversations, stopping only for a few instances to check if a public-boat could be seen in the distance.

Nauseated from the oscillation of the dock, I attempted to get outside onto the firm pavement, but could not move. I heard Davide laughing again, and couldn't help but think that even though we were friends, and spent a lot of time together, when we met on the street, Davide often pretended he did not see me. I began to think of the day we met, when I fell in love for the first time, when I felt a jolt that rearranged things inside me.

Falling in Love

It was a windy, bright spring day, and the sweet scent of lilacs permeated through the open windows of Signora Maria's house. With my homework completed, I felt content to play with my pencil, twist it, and sketch small butterflies on the white pages of my workbook. I listened to the murmurs of the students all around me as I waited for Tina to finish her homework so we could meet our friends on the bridge of *San Pietro Martire*.

At the bridge, we leaned on the steel rail, watched the boats swishing by, and talked to friends, relatives and acquaintances who stopped to say a few words as they walked by.

We told our names to the old ladies who came out of the church. Not really sure who we were, they asked, as if it were the most natural thing to do, "Are you Lidia's daughter?"

When we told them no, we were so and so's daughters, the elderly ladies exclaimed, "Oh. . .you all are getting so big. I remember when your mother used to bring you to kindergarten. Well, now I see the resemblance. Yes, you do have your mother's eyes."

The old ladies talked about an incident that happened during their childhood, a short story in which our mothers were involved as well. Satisfied to have made a connection with the younger generation, happy that they could still find something to talk about, they said *arrivederci* and went on their way, smiling.

There, on that bridge, Tina and I met Davide for the first time.

"Look, he is coming towards us," Sele whispered.

A young, short, thin boy, whom I had never noticed before, walked, smiling towards us, beige trench coat flowing in the wind, felt hat placed on his head Jean Gabin style. As he walked, he lifted his hat, exposing his thick ebony hair parted on the side. He twirled the hat in the air, catching it as his eyes scanned our faces.

Hat in his hand, he ran up the stairs and stopped in front of Tina and me. He shook our hands. He brushed his bangs off his eyes. He smiled, and the right side of his mouth showed off his beauty mark. He looked at us with his bright, dark penetrating eyes and introduced himself, "*Ciao, piacere*, Davide."

He stood so close to my space. I shook his hand, blushed, mumbled my name, and lowered my eyes. Tina shook his hand, showed her white front teeth, and uttered in her spunky crystal voice, "*Piacere*, Tina."

We began to walk and talk. We stopped under the church cloister and talked some more. Aldo, Davide's best friend, joined us as well. After a while, I nudged Tina on the arm. I wanted to discuss the strange feeling that aroused my soul, and awakened within me a sentiment I was not familiar with; a feeling which paralyzed my train of thoughts when Davide was near.

Tina and I left. We crossed the *Ponte Lungo*, and pranced through *Fondamenta degli Angeli* toward the cemetery.

We turned at the archway in *Fondamenta degli Angeli* and ran on the tall, unkempt damp grass of the field. We sat on our step, outside of the cemetery, talking about our feelings, and what we didn't say to each other aloud, we understood.

We talked about Davide when we met with our girlfriends at Marta and Sele's house. We all tried to guess who among us was his favorite girl. It was hard to guess because he flirted with everyone. In a span of a few hours, he could be Prince Charming and talk to each of us as if we were the only girls who mattered to him. Or if we met him on the *fondamenta* and he didn't feel like talking to us, he would divert his eyes even though we passed only inches away from each other.

Tina and I walked by his house at noon. We walked by his house at four. At times, we walked by his house late into the evening, hoping to catch a glimpse of him, or just to hear his voice.

A few weeks after Tina and I met him, we watched the boys play soccer in the church field, and after the game, we waited for Davide and Aldo at the entrance door.

"Davide, we would like to know which of us you like the best," Sele asked in her sweet voice, batting her long eyelashes in a lady-like manner.

"Let me see what I can do," Davide said.

Davide glanced at us, at Sele who was dressed all prim and proper in her older sister's lime green sweater. He pondered for a few minutes, nodded his head as if to say, let me think about it for a while.

He acted as if he were expecting the request, as if it were the most natural thing for him to do, to categorize us, to prioritize us with numbers just as he would animals or material things.

"Let me think about it. Let's meet tomorrow, and I will give you my answer," he said.

The next day, we met as usual at the church grounds. We talked as we sat by the white Romanesque colonnades, on the brittle, red brick, and waited for Davide to say something.

I could not follow the conversation I was having with Aldo. Pretending to be listening, I laughed when Tina slapped Aldo on the head. With my thoughts and peripheral sight on Davide, I fidgeted with my white handkerchief as I wrapped and unwrapped it around my fingers. I slouched forward, elbow on my knee, chin resting on my fingers trying to imitate Sele. With my hands flat on the bricks, I swung my legs back and forth. I tried to act more grown up, more sophisticated, as I waited for Davide's announcement.

Finally, Davide handed the small piece of white paper with a list of names on it to Sele. He looked at us one by one.

His eyes turned in my direction.

He looked at me through a faint smile. My heart raced, and I wanted to die. He looked at me and. . .I thought I would be first on the list.

Sele opened the small piece of paper and read in her calm and collected voice, "Sele, Dina, Marta, Rosa, Tina." Tina was the last one, and I wasn't even on the list. Tina clutched my arm, walked toward the *fondamenta*, said to our friends, "See you tomorrow," and waved.

We walked in silence for a while. Tina consoled me in her pragmatic way. She laughed at the fact that she was last and said that the advantage of being last, or not on the list, was that now we could act with the boys just like good friends. Those were not her words. They were her grandmother's. Her grandmother had said that it was so much better at our age to be good friends with the boys than to be *morosi,* boyfriend and girlfriend. And that it would be too much pressure to have a boyfriend, so we should have fun instead.

Tina repeated her grandmother's words a couple of times, but coming from a twelve year old, they rang untrue.

Lost in Adolescence

"*Signorina* Anna, the boat is here." I glanced at the man behind me and nodded. I began to move forward with all of the other passengers but winced back instead. People began to push and shove their way into the boat, hoping to find an empty seat.

Aldo's head, which towered over everyone, disappeared inside the boat. I tried to push toward the front, but once I stepped on the boat, I could not move, my body pressed against the outer stainless steel rail. I turned on my axis, keeping one arm dangling in front while with the other I held my books and the umbrella.

The boat began to navigate towards Venice. Trying to avoid the wind, I lowered my head, and gazed at the capricious, foamy water. I shivered. I wished I had gone to help Papa instead of going to school. I felt safe with him. He made me feel important. Like Gabri, I did not like secretarial work, and would have preferred working in a shop in Venice selling clothes, perfume, or leather goods. I often imagined myself behind a counter, all dressed up, talking to people, not to numbers.

Numbers gave me a nervous stomach and a confused head. I never could figure out the word problems. My mind became one fuzzy mess when I had to calculate how many hours the boat going downstream would take to go from point A to point B compared to the boat that went upstream. No matter how many drawings, and how many times Signora Maria explained it to me, I just could not get the drift of it. The truth was that I did not care how long it took the two boats to travel up or down stream. Or that mathematics expanded one's logical thinking. I was good at simple multiplication, addition, subtraction, division and percentages. I calculated percentages in my mind faster than anyone I knew. And those were all of the numbers I cared to play with. No, I did not want to become a secretary and be cooped up in an office all day.

A jolt startled me. The boat stopped to pick up a monk at the small island of *San Michele,* the Venetian Cemetery. I saw the monk, holding his sandals, lifting his coarse, brown robe, trying to squeeze his way into the already over crowded boat.

"Move, move forward," the attendant shouted. "Make room, here! One more person, come on, come on. . .move," he repeated.

The poor Franciscan hung on the rail for dear life. Covered only with his rudimentary robe, he shivered in the damp, gloomy autumn weather.

I stared at the steel water, at the thousand small bursts of tumultuous, foamy caps emerging from within the Venetian lagoon. I gazed at the distant, gray buildings of Marghera's factories, at the bridge that connected the island of Venice with the mainland, and at the closed shutters of the apartment buildings at *Fondamente Nuove* in Venice. The sea, the sky, the buildings, and objects in between were painted with the same gray color, except of different hues. Everything looked like one depressing expansion. Like a painting with a thousand different emotions imprinted in it, waiting to be defined and dissected into clear, concise ideas. That is how I felt. Lost in the tumult of adolescence, in the first burst of love for Davide, and in the horrified thought that I was not ready for the imminent math test.

I wanted to go back home, to run to Papa's factory, to be with Papa, and to listen to his tenor voice sing *La Traviata*. I imagined Papa stopping what he was doing to observe a small sparrow in search of seeds or admiring the ducks passing by, taking turns to lead the flock at intervals.

"Look, a sparrow coming back to build its nest. Pretty soon it will give life. What a wonder. . .what a miracle life is," Papa always said, emphasizing aloud the magnitude of the power of God within nature's realm.

I turned my neck to stare at the Franciscan's bare cranium, and asked myself why should Franciscans follow such a rigid regiment.

Mama said that Papa, when young, thought of becoming a Franciscan Monk. He even packed his suitcase and went to stay at the monastery.

Everyone worried, except his mother.

"Do not worry," she said to her family. "Tomorrow, Nico will be back home. He needs people around."

Grandmother was right. Papa returned home after spending just one night at the monastery.

The math test came to mind again. My stomach and head hurt. I decided that on the way to school I would stop by the church of *San Giovanni e Paolo* to pray and to ask Saint Anthony to help me.

I thought of what Papa would have done in my situation. I knew that Papa never worried about earthly things. If he needed assistance, he stopped by the church of *San Pietro Martire*, stood in front of the image of his favorite saint and asked for a miracle.

In Murano, we proved our allegiance to God, bartering material goods or penances for divine intervention.

Bartering with the Saints

Before I went to school each morning, veil on my head, I tiptoed into *San Pietro Martire* church, together with my friends. I genuflected in front of the cross, then walked to the statue of Saint Anthony and asked him to grant me a small miracle.

I prayed that my teacher would not call on me and that she would not ask me any questions in front of the class. Every Friday, I prayed that she might postpone the scheduled test. In exchange, I promised to go to the vespers for a whole week. . .a month.

Renzo's mother, Mama's friend, Lola, asked St. Anthony to find her a husband. She worried about remaining a spinster because all of her friends were already engaged or married.

On Sundays, instead of listening to the priest's sermon, Signora Lola stared at every eligible bachelor. She fantasized about meeting on the *fondamenta* the tall young man who sat at the altar, singing his heart out on cue from Sister Pacifica. Signora Lola did not know him, but she knew his family owned the grocery store across the bridge. Her mother went there when she needed fast service and her regular store was over crowded.

When Signora Lola came to our house for a brief visit, she always told us stories about St. Anthony and how he helped her throughout her life.

Signora Lola spoke like our neighbor's radio, morning, noon and night; a radio, not like our TV, but one which talked even if you did not pound on it to make it work. A devout woman, she carried images in her wallet of all of the saints who gave her strength.

At twenty-three, and still single, Signora Lola decided she needed help from above.

"Teresa, do you remember the time I decided to go to Padova to give money to St. Anthony so I could ask him for a husband?" Signora Lola said. "You know, I laugh now, but I worried about remaining a spinster, so that's why I put my trust in St. Anthony."

She must have given quite a bit of money to St. Anthony because he had a reputation for being *interessato*—a Saint who grants your wishes only in exchange for healthy monetary contributions.

On the way back home from visiting St. Anthony in Padova, Signora Lola dropped one of her magazines on the floor. It opened to the horoscope page. The young, tall man she had eyed at the altar on Sundays picked up the magazine and read his horoscope aloud to her. That day, he began a conversation with Signora Lola that lasted for more than forty years.

Mama said with a chuckle that St. Anthony chose well for her, as Signora Lola was very happy. And so, I think, were St. Anthony's administrators of assistance with her donation.

Not all saints were *interessati*. *Santa Rita* granted the impossible without expecting anything in return. Although at times, she did not mind a small token of appreciation.

If you were scared of thunder and lightening, you prayed respectively to St. Simon and St. Barbara. That is what my cousin Giulio must have done the day lighting struck the iron frame of his bed.

Giulio lay awake one summer night listening to the rain splashing on the roof-tops while he stared out the bedroom window. Mama said St. Barbara must have been watching over him because even though the edge of his bed burned, he did not have a mark on him, not even a blister.

Papa's favorite Saint was his namesake St. Nicolò.

Nicolò di Bari had been the patron Saint of the *Vetrai Muranesi* for many centuries. He actually was not a native of Bari, as the Baresi stole his body from Myra around 1087. St. Nicolò had been a peddler who procured the dowry for poor, young brides. But most important in my life and the lives of all the children in Murano, St. Nicolò brought us gifts on the sixth of every December.

St. Nicolò, most of the time, did not bring toys to my siblings and me. When we got up, on the sixth of December, we would all jump up and down amidst ooohhhs and aaahhhs, happy at the sight of Mama's huge green dish filled with fresh fruits, apples, oranges, winter pears, tangerines, hazelnuts, salted pumpkin seeds, peanuts, dried figs and dates. If we were lucky, we found a toothbrush or an occasional flashlight or a small toy.

One year Gabri, Margherita, Giuliana and I asked for a doll. Gabri said there was no harm in asking. With her customary manner that told us she knew it all, she said that we should write a note to St. Nicolò requesting a big doll. Gabri even dictated what color dress to request and described her dream doll in minute details. Gabri and Mama must have had a conversation with Saint Nicolò because on the sixth of December, on the kitchen table by the big dish full of fruits sat a huge doll, decked in a long, blue dress with a white straw-hat tied with a blue satin ribbon under her chin. The doll's long blond hair was combed in small ringlets that hung down to the top of her puffy sleeves. Her big blue eyes opened and closed as we moved the doll up and down, and her arms and legs moved forward and backward. If you held her by the arms, you could pretend she was taking steps like a small baby.

As it happened, St. Nicolò had sent a peddler Mama's way.

A few days before the sixth of December, Gelmina heard someone shouting from the street, *"Pignate vecie, forchete, scugeri…beie done. Vegni a veder che meravegia de roba che ve dago!"* "Old pans, forks, spoons. . .beautiful ladies. Come and see what marvelous merchandise I have for you."

"Signora Teresa, do we have any old pots and pans to give the peddler? Alice downstairs exchanged a few old things for a nice set of dishes," Gelmina said to Mama when she heard the raucous voice coming from the street.

That's how it was in those days. Peddlers came to the house to sell and cajole you into giving them old merchandise in exchange for new. They came like ambulant vendors on a huge boat, which everyone in Venice and in the nearby islands used for transporting fresh produce, furniture, combustibles, and chemicals the artisans used to create their glass art works.

The peddlers lived on their boats. Their faces, wrinkled from too much sun, rain, wind and snow, resembled the rough leather goods they bartered for old iron. In the summer, they slept in the open air under the starry sky. In winter, they docked their boats under a bridge to protect themselves from the occasional snow or thunderstorm.

Dressed in second-hand clothes too big for their short, skinny bodies, they covered their foreheads with red bandanas. They docked the boats in the *fondamenta* and walked around Murano. At the top of their voices, they called for the housewives to poke their heads out their windows to make sure they did not miss a bargain.

One day, our neighbor, Signora Alice came for coffee after lunch, with a sample-set of dishes the peddler had given her in exchange for heavy, old black iron frying pans. Even though she and Mama were careful to speak in riddles, thinking that we were not listening, I understood that the doll had come from the peddler.

Perhaps that is what St. Nicolò did—guided the ambulant vendors to go by before the sixth of December so we could have the doll.

Perhaps St. Nicolò inspired Mama and Papa's good friend, Signora Marina, another one of my eleven godparents, to always remember us children. She gave Mama the occasional flashlight or small toy to put on the kitchen table next to the fruit dish.

Signora Marina was generous, not only with Mama, but with all of Murano's inhabitants. She and her husband first opened a small appliance store which they enlarged as their business escalated into a profitable operation. Mama told us Signora Marina's success was not an accident. She was successful because she treated each customer as a member of her immediate family, with decency and respect.

If Signora Marina found out that her customers could not make the small monthly payments on the merchandise they purchased in her store, she lent them the money because she did not want her customers to pay the penalty.

"Signora Marina is an angel from heaven," Papa said when he was certain he had our undivided attention.

Papa loved talking about the small miracles of life. He perceived any kindness a wonder, a miracle. He savored life one spoonful at a time, just like he did Mama's soups.

I often mused about how many people Mama and Papa could squeeze into our small apartment. If there were not enough chairs to seat all of our guests, we used the small seat from the bathroom, the two extra chairs

Mama had inherited from her own mother, and the wooden fruit crates Mama kept by the kitchen stove full of small twigs to light the morning fire. No one seemed to mind. Whoever sat on the crates cracked many jokes. At times, there was not enough to eat for everyone, yet Papa and Mama gracefully extended an invitation to whoever was around during lunch or dinner, especially if they felt the person could use the attention. Mama just added more water to the broth, or cooked more pasta.

Papa made a point of celebrating life.

St. Nicolò was a day of festivity and Mama's relatives came for dinner every year to celebrate Nicolo's day and to dance the night away to the old fashioned tunes of the *Quadriglia* and the *Mazzurca*.

After dinner, Great Aunt Nice called the steps of the *Quadriglia*. From the middle of the living room, Great Aunt Nice curtsied. Decked in the black dress she wore every day in commemoration of her father's death, which had occurred years before I was born, she moved her arms as if she were the director of a dance school. One hand in the air, she held the index finger and the thumb together as she let the other three fingers fall freely towards the palms of her hands one after the other. Her movements were delicate, her voice decisive. She called out the steps and tapped her feet to dictate the rhythm. On cue, everyone joined hands with a partner, walked two by two in a circular motion, skipped in unison, and turned at Great Aunt Nice's command.

It was always fun to celebrate with Papa, and to listen to him talk about life's small wonders.

A Small Miracle

One day, during summer vacation, Antonio, Gabri and I went *Dietro Gli Orti # 7* to work at Papa's new *laboratorio* as we needed to fill an order of mirrors that had come from France.

Papa sat in front of his small motor wheel, engraving pieces of long rectangular glass, which when completed, were transformed into mirrors. He sang songs from *Aida*. Verdi was his favorite composer. Antonio and I glued silver and gold foil onto the edge of the mirror's wooden frame and shined the finished product.

At mid-morning, Gabri, who had been in the office sorting the bills, walked by Papa.

"It's the end of the month," she said. "We have many bills, but no money to pay them."

Papa stopped working and turned towards us.

"Don't worry, *bambini*. God will take care of us."

Antonio, who had the same personality as Mama, shook his head all serious as he glanced in my direction.

"You live in the clouds, Papa," Gabri said. "We have bills to pay, and you tell us that God will take care of us. Don't you understand that we have to pay the bills, now." Gabri walked back into the office and slammed the door.

I felt embarrassed. I wanted to run to the bank and get the fifty thousand lire Uncle Paolo had put there for my birthday and give it to Papa, but I was afraid Uncle Paolo would scold me for taking the money out of the bank. When Uncle Paolo had handed me the blue book, he had cast the brightest smile over me—as if having money in the bank was my lifelong dream—and he made me promise I would not spend the money.

"Anna, look," he said with complacency. "I opened a bank account for you."

All I could do when Uncle Paolo handed me the bank book was to swallow hard, hold back my tears, give him a fake smile, take a few steps forward and kiss him on the cheek. I was angry because for my birthday I had wanted to buy a pair of small heeled, red shoes to wear on Sunday to church or to the movies. Unaware of how I felt inside, Uncle Paolo gave me a sermon on the importance of saving money, and of the interest that would accrue over the years. The first chance I got, I blasted out of Uncle's office and ran as fast as I could through the *fondamenta*, over *Ponte Lungo*, till I stepped into Mama's kitchen, bank book in hand. I began to cry. Muddling my words, I explained my ordeal to Mama.

"Anna, Anna," Mama said, "what happened?"

I told Mama I did not like Uncle Paolo. He did not understand things. I did not want a bank account. I wanted the money instead. I wanted to buy the red shoes I had seen in a store's window in Venice.

And now, Gabri was upset. Papa needed money, and I could not help him. I would have rather given it to Papa, but he would never have allowed it.

Papa did not answer when Gabri slammed the office door. He sighed and looked at the sky through the window. Perhaps Papa did not hear Gabri. Perhaps he was praying hard. According to Gabri, we needed money to pay the bills. According to Papa, divine intervention was needed. At the precise moment Gabri slammed the office door, the doorbell rang.

Antonio ran to open it.

I approached the door and heard an unfamiliar voice saying, "Don't worry son. Don't worry. I have money to pay for the mirrors. Can I come in?"

Antonio must have looked pretty desperate for a total stranger to tell him that he had money to purchase the merchandise. The stranger must have thought a thirteen-year-old boy should have had a lighter heart, and that he should not have resembled a ghost when he opened the door to greet the customers.

Through a chink in the working room door, I saw two black shiny shoes step in. The person wore a black smock with a row of small buttons in the front and a white starched collar tight around a short neck. I saw the flushed, tired face of an old man, panting and rubbing the top of his bald head with a light blue handkerchief.

"I'm getting old, son," the man said as he placed one hand on Antonio's arm. "I'm very tired."

Antonio stepped aside. His expression softened as he made room for the visitor to enter. I understood why Antonio showed his disappointment. I also understood the reassurance on the stranger's part. For the first time in my life, and in Papa's as well, a priest came with money to purchase merchandise, an event tantamount to going to the moon.

The priest entered the huge working room.

"*Eilà*, Padre," Papa said. "Do come in."

"This is Padre Alberto," Antonio shouted to Papa. "He came to buy some mirrors."

Papa made much fuss over Padre Alberto. As Papa ushered him into the display room, he lit the glittering chandeliers that adorned the ceiling.

"Padre Alberto," Papa said. "What can we help you with?"

"My feet hurt," Padre Alberto said. "I walked all over Murano until someone directed me here. Can I have a chair? I'm old and tired."

"Padre Alberto, do you want a glass of water?" Papa said. "Anna, bring a glass of water for the Padre, please."

Antonio ran to grab a chair from the corner of the room while I went to get a glass of water.

The showroom was cooler than the other rooms because Gabri closed the door and shutters to keep the scorching heat out. Padre Alberto said that earlier, when he walked on the sunny *fondamenta*, his heart began to pound and he had felt lightheaded. Padre Alberto sat in the blue padded chair. His over-protected body perspired as if he were taking a sauna. He wiped his sweaty leathery face with his handkerchief, then rested his scruffy hand on his long black vest. In his raspy tone of voice, he gave Papa the measurements of the three mirrors he needed.

Gabri entered the display room walking in a ceremonial fashion. She looked so grown up in her black and white rimmed glasses, hair pinned up into a chignon, bangs framing her scarred forehead. Even if she did have a fine, young expressive face, she looked much older than sixteen because her large bosom was the first thing people noticed.

She introduced herself, bowed and lowered her head as she did when entering a church. Gabri took a few steps towards Padre Alberto. She addressed him in that special tone of voice she often used around priests, monks and nuns; a voice that told us she had put on her holy halo.

I could not help but think of how different her demeanor had been just a few moments before when she confronted Papa about the bills. Our family often observed with amusement the vicissitudes she resorted to when she needed something or wanted to make an impression. Gabri could alter her personality with the same swiftness Papa transformed a glass full of wine into an empty one during his magic tricks.

Papa and Gabri suggested several choices of mirrors to Padre Alberto. He could create his very own mirror, putting together the frame of #342 with the colors of #355, or with the beveled glass details of #360. Papa could place different colored roses on the crystal oval mirror or engrave a floral design on the mosaic pieces that contoured the frame of the rectangular one. But Padre Alberto did not want to create his own rendition of an already finished artwork. Exhausted, Padre Alberto decided on three of the mirrors that hung on the wall. Gabri, with utmost efficiency, wrote all the details on an order-form while Antonio and I watched.

"Padre Alberto," Papa said as he glanced at his watch, "have you eaten yet?"

"No, son. I'll probably get a sandwich at the train station. I'm going back to Castelfranco on the four o'clock train."

The idea of eating a sandwich at the train station did not appeal to Papa. It would have been just as bad to have thrown Papa under the train and left him there to suffer.

A sandwich from the train station would not do. Never!

"Gabri, Antonio, Anna, let's go," Papa said. "Padre Alberto is coming home with us."

The Padre complained a little then tagged along through the *fondamenta* in the scorching summer heat.

During lunch, Padre Alberto talked about his parish. He said that every year he had a bazaar, but they did not collect much money. The church needed a lot of fixing up, and even though his parishioners were very good, they brought him vegetables, chickens and eggs, instead of money.

"We do not die of hunger in the country. Do you know bambini," he said to make us laugh, "that in the country, the belly of a priest is the cemetery of the chickens?"

Papa and Padre Alberto talked like old friends. In between the meat and the fruit, Papa talked about the *Vetrai Muranesi*. He explained about their generosity, and how the *Vetrai Muranesi* gave pieces of glass objects to every priest and nun who came to Murano and asked for a donation.

After lunch, Padre Alberto taught us a funny song about a small house made of sticks with walls of fine paper, without windows, without a kitchen, without bedrooms.

The whole family sang along with the Padre.

"Padre Alberto, why don't you stay with us for a few days," Papa said as we uttered the last few notes. "Tomorrow Antonio and Pietro can take you around to all the factories to get glass objects for your annual bazaar."

"Teresa," he added, "can we put a mattress in the living room for Padre Alberto?"

Good thing that Mama did not hear Gelmina mumble under her breath, "*Eh, si. Unca el prete ne vol!*" "Oh, yes. Even the priest we need." Priests were always one of Gelmina's pet peeves, although she did sing and enjoy Padre Alberto's funny song.

"Oh no. No, no, no. I don't want to disturb you, Nico," Padre Alberto said.

We all looked at Mama, at Papa, at Padre Alberto.

"Signora Teresa," the Padre said to Mama, "I have to catch the four o'clock train. I better go."

"If you do not mind sleeping on a mattress on the floor," Mama replied.

Padre Alberto did not mind. Sure, he made some more excuses and declined the invitation, but Papa insisted because he said he could tell Padre Alberto was smiling inside. Padre Alberto missed the four o'clock train back to Castelfranco. He missed the next morning's train, the afternoon one, and the one after that.

Until Papa received word of Padre Alberto's death, the Padre returned to Murano every year, slept on the mattress on our living room floor, ate with us, sang his funny song, and went around to all of the factories.

Antonio and Pietro accompanied him, and carried the glass objects people donated each year to Padre Alberto for his annual bazaar.

Angels, Saints, Jesus, Mary and Joseph, were the honorary members of the *Muranesi* families. One could tell the members of the Holy Family just about anything that came to mind without fear of being ridiculed. One could ask them for money, for a husband, help with a math test, and anything else that struck one's fancy without having to worry of paying them back. Papa, Mama, Gelmina and we children knew that help from above was just around the corner from where we stood.

Papa Nico engraving a vase at work

A Prayer to St. Anthony

As I furtively scanned the faces of people on the boat, I heard Papa's voice in my mind, like a broken record that turns and turns the duration of a lifetime, reiterating the same words, albeit, each time with a different intonation in his voice.

"God can move the world for you. All you have to do is ask Him."

I began to shiver when a gust of wind blew my wet scarf from my head. My thoughts were interrupted by the boat attendant, *"Venezia. . .Fondamente Nuove. . .Fine corsa! Fine corsa!"*

I looked up and saw the *Fondamente Nuove* approaching. I turned towards the exit, anxious to get out before Aldo and Davide.

In Venice, I was the first to disembark. I wanted to walk to church by myself and pray by Saint Anthony's chapel. When I arrived at the church, I could not open the front portal. The force of the water against the door prevented it from moving. I checked the side door. It was wide open. I carefully stepped down onto the carpet of water and stood immobile for a moment, aware of the profound silence within its walls. The church was cold, austere and deserted. The long benches in front of the main altar, where people genuflected during the Sunday Masses, were under water. The folding chairs rested on elevated wooden planks built especially for the high tide. Everything was dark, but for the one, small red light on the main tabernacle—the symbol of the presence of Christ.

From a distance, I noticed a faint glow on the rusted metal stand in front of St. Anthony's statue. I walked by the Virgin Mary's chapel and stopped to dip my hand in the holy water. I bowed my head in reverence and tapped my right, cupped hand on my forehead, chest, and both shoulders while I recited, "In the name of the Father, the Son, and the Holy Spirit." I trod the length of the church to the chapel adjacent to the main altar.

It felt spooky to be there by myself. In the past, when the rays of sun illuminated and enveloped the interior of the church, and the sound of the organ resounded in the distance, an aura of mysticism permeated throughout, buttressing even more the inherent feelings of faith I felt.

Now, I was not so sure. I felt cold. Only general dissatisfaction stemmed from within. At times, it seemed easier not to study, but it was a lie I told myself when I did not want to make the effort. I knew that if I tried a bit harder I could have done well in school. Instead, I took what I imagined to be the easy way out and prayed that the teacher would not call on me.

And there was the issue of Davide. There were days when I could not think of anything else: my mind and body so full of him that I could not swallow one single bite of food, nor register a single thought other than where is he, now? What is he doing? What is he thinking?

Questions flowed into my head, but all I could do was make up the answers. I imagined meeting Davide by the bridge, talking to him at Signora Maria's house, or holding hands at the movies. I plotted what time to leave my house so I would arrive at *Ponte San Pietro Martire* as Davide came back from school. That way, our paths would cross at the foot of the bridge. I fantasized that he smiled at me as we crossed the bridge and walked the three meters to his house. He would utter, "I'll see you later." And those simple imaginary words would reverberate in my head, bouncing around for hours.

I gave all kinds of meaning to those words.

"I'll see you later," was like he had caressed my face, stroked my bangs aside with the tips of his fingers, leaned over to give me a soft kiss. I spent an infinite amount of time creating a relationship, which was solely the figment of my imagination.

A solitary lost bird flew into the church. It flapped its wings, looking for a place to land. I watched as it brushed and dragged its tiny body against the façade. Uncertain of where to go, it circumnavigated the massive church walls. I stared preoccupied, and in my mind, I guided the lost creature out into the open air. I cheered the bird on until it landed on top of a marble statue's head by the open side door. Afraid to make a move, the frail bird kept still for a few seconds as its little eyes scanned the room with a puzzled look. It turned its head left, right, left, right as if it were an electric toy. With a sudden burst of renewed energy, the plumed bird dove outside.

I breathed a sigh of relief.

I turned around to face the St. Anthony's statue, and with my hand, I fished for the twenty lire I had in the pocket of my raincoat. I dropped the two coins in the metal locked box attached to the stand. Clink! Clink! An echo, the vibration of my insignificant supplication, the sound of my small donation, resounded throughout. I lit the short white candle. With a nervous stomach, my eyes fixed on the glow of the flickering lights, I prayed, then left.

Outside, I looked to see if Davide and Aldo had already passed by. I trod through the water with small steps, not really concerned about being late for school, sure that the high tide would be a good excuse to arrive late. I walked by Tina's school, but no one was in sight.

The *calle* were crowded with people walking in both directions.

"*Gente,* people, move to the side. Come on, I don't have all day. The bread is getting cold," a man who transported the fresh bread to his satellite shops, carrying it on a huge hand truck, whooped at the top of his voice.

"Ladies, are you waiting for the sun to come out or for the water to go down? Move. Ladies, ladies, be careful not to ruin your pretty dresses," he added in his own nonsensical rhetoric.

On the bridges people stood still for a few minutes. They looked around at the ornate gothic windows of the palaces that stood, partially swallowed by the water, undeterred in spite of their wet feet. I watched the shop owners and their employees moving their merchandise, sweeping the water out of their shops. They stopped for a few seconds to chat, to console each other about the repercussions of the flood, on their losses. A man fell on his back, sprawled limbs, trying to wrench open his swollen front door. Fighting his way up, he cursed at the door, at the Virgin Mary, at God and all of the saints.

My thoughts turned again to the math test, but I was distracted by someone singing the aria from Rigoletto. The tenor voice sounded very much like Papa's voice. I could swear it was Papa's voice trying to find a bright spot amidst the gloomy surroundings. I looked at the gray, foamy clouds roaming in the firmament, and thought I saw the shape of a dark puffy, spongy face laughing. Even if the clouds looked like a gathering of open laughing mouths, they always ended up crying. Perhaps the clouds laughed at what they saw and heard on the earth.

Gelmina often told us children when we were having a good time, "Be careful not to laugh too hard because in the end, you will end up crying!"

She must have been talking about the time, on a hot summer's day, when Tina, Sele and I went swimming in a deserted canal with our clothes on, unbeknownst to our mothers. By the time we reached the center of the canal, we were laughing so hard I almost drowned. In the end, the three of us became so scared we cried.

Now, the clouds were very low. From the top of the bridge, it seemed I could almost touch them with the tips of my fingers. Papa probably would have said that he felt "sandwiched" between the sea and the clouds; while Mama would have added that there was no way he would ever get away from thinking about food.

The word sandwich made me think of the day Gabri asked at the dinner table how could God, Jesus and the Holy Spirit be three in one. Papa had explained about water, ice and vapor. They were made of the same ingredients, yet they were physically different. Gabri's cheeks and nose twitched up a bit, as she thought about it for a few seconds. Satisfied with the explanation, she turned her head to look at Pietro fighting with Margherita for the only piece of bread on the table.

Pietro was protesting. He wanted the last piece of bread for himself because he explained to Margherita, he had gone to the store to buy it. Mama, listening to his reasoning, just shook her head in disbelief. She had sent Pietro to buy seven *panini* at the corner store before it closed. On the way home, Pietro had eaten six of them. Now he claimed the one single *panino* on the table. He couldn't help himself. He was a true Marchini.

Always hungry, with a gargantuan appetite, Pietro made sure he got more than his share.

"Pietro, let your sister have half." Having said that, Papa continued talking about the wonders of nature. Water going up, water coming down. Just like life. Up and down.

Deeply engaged in my own reveries that warmed my heart, I tried to bypass a narrow area in the *calle* where traffic was at its fullest.

A throng of people blocked the *calle* trying to enter a coffee shop where the water had not yet reached because it was two steps higher than the street level. The scent of baked pastries and coffee permeated the *calle*, luring the customers in. People stood in line outside, waving their money as if they were at the Stock Market Exchange. They pushed, chatted and commented on the weather situation with ardor. They waved their thousand *lire* as if it were their life's investment, as if the rest of their life depended on that piping hot espresso and the delicious croissant. If I didn't feel so cold and wet, I could have found the vignette humorous. I tried to ignore the smell of pastries. I inserted my hand in my pocket to see if I had any change left, even though I knew I had dropped my last twenty lire in the metal box to pay for the candle. As I squeezed between the brick wall and the people standing, I heard someone calling my name.

"Anna, Anna." Startled, I recoiled a few steps and looked back to see if I recognized anyone. I rubbed my eyes to clear my vision and tried to decipher if the sound came from the far back or from above.

"Where are you?" I heard someone say. I noticed a lady looking up, talking to an elderly signora who leaned against the windowsill of a third story apartment window.

"Anna," she called again. "Can you get me *due panini, per piacere?* Do me this favor so that I do not have to go out today."

"You don't have to come up," she added. "Ring the doorbell, and I'll lower the basket."

As Signora Anna yelled back that, of course, she would be happy to buy her the two pieces of bread, the elderly lady lowered a small straw basket. When it reached Signora Anna's eye level, Signora Anna took the money from the basket and said, *arrivederci a presto.*

I arrived at school. The mastodon door was shut. A few students stood talking by the marble well in the middle of the square. I did not recognize anyone. I tried to pry the door open, but one girl shouted, "The school is closed. They sent everyone home."

My shoulders relaxed, the tense muscles between my eyebrows softened, and I breathed a sigh of relief.

"Thank you, St. Anthony," I mouthed. I did not have to take the math test.

"Thank you," I repeated as I looked up at the sky and stared at the dark clouds.

Now, I could go to help Papa at the factory. I regretted not connecting with Tina in the morning, and wondered if Tina's school had been closed as well.

"*Permesso, permesso,*" called a worker pushing a wheelbarrow full of Venetian Masks trying to go through the narrow pass before the Bridge *Dei Bareteri*. At the sound of his voice, I stepped to the side. A cat staring at me from a windowsill startled me. I ducked, skipped past it and almost lost my equilibrium. Water entered my boots while the bottom of my raincoat dragged through the murky water.

I felt sick.

My body shivered. My teeth chattered. I touched my forehead and neck with my right hand, as Mama did, to find out if I had a fever. At the boat station, I had heard people say that there were many cases of *influenza* in Murano. Perhaps the cold air in the *vaporetto* triggered the chills.

I walked a little faster and thought that it would be better if I went home to warm up by the kitchen stove. At Papa's factory there were three small electric stoves, but no central heating. In winter, the workers kept their coats on. I wondered how Papa, Gabri, Antonio and the two workers were going to package the merchandise, place it in huge wooden boxes, seal it with long nails, and ship it that day. The high tide slowed things down, but Papa was a determined person, and if he promised to ship it, he would do everything in his power to get the order on its way.

In the end, I decided to go home. I knew that Gelmina would prepare a hot water bottle for me to take to bed, and Mama would make chicken broth, give me an aspirin, tuck me in, and tell me to sleep.

I did not want to be sick. Monday and Tuesday were school holidays, All Saints Day, and the Feast of the Dead. Throughout the day, the *Muranesi* went to the cemetery in a procession with huge bouquets of flowers, to pray and pay their respects to their loved ones. People walked around, not only near the tombs of their relatives, but they also stopped by the tombs of the people who had touched their lives in some special way. On that day, as Mama, Papa, my siblings and I meandered through the cemetery, I listened with curiosity to Mama's stories as she recounted incidents of people whose pictures I recognized only because of the familiar names engraved on the headstones.

High Tide in Murano

The Cemetery

The cemetery is a perennial place of rest for the dead, and a place of comfort for the living. People went there to pay their respects, to shine the marble tombs of their loved ones to a mirror luster, to insure that every petal and leaf was placed on the vases just so, and that no wild greenery grew to ruin the intended artistic compositions.

Many times during the day, when Tina and I went to the cemetery in Murano—a square area surrounded by four tall brick walls—we sat on its steps and listened to the faint sounds of hammers pounding on wooden boxes coming from the factories' courtyard, the distant voices of the workers barking orders at each other, and workers singing Italian folklore songs or popular opera pieces in their tenor voices. From the cemetery's entrance, we could see a few residential buildings in the distance, and the reddish brick *façades* of the glass factories with their huge glass windows. We watched people walking in and out of the cemetery, and sometimes in the spring, we made the rounds inside to admire the pretty headstones, the fresh flowers and the pictures on the tombstones.

Inside we walked on the dirt paths filled with little pebbles and listened to the crunchy noises our shoes made. Arm in arm, Tina and I strolled between the thick trunks of the tall cypresses that lined the gravel paths. We heeded the sounds of the birds swishing through the branches where the small sparrows and other birds built their shelters.

As we walked, we felt the tepid gentle breeze caress our faces, and smelled the scent of the roses and violets people planted on the graves. Like everyone else who went to visit, we felt connected to the smiling faces glued on the tombs because in Murano almost everyone was your distant cousin. At times, Tina and I didn't recognize the people in the tombstone pictures, but we did recognize their last names and their physiognomy.

Perhaps it was the peaceful atmosphere inside the four walls which gave people comfort and energy afterwards. Perhaps it was the walk to and from the cemetery, but somehow after their visits, people felt inclined to chat and socialize with whoever was around.

The day Tina and I stood by the cemetery's front gate waiting for Tina's brother, Tulio, to come back from his bike-ride, Clara and Emilia, my third cousins, came out of the cemetery, laughing. Not a loud laugh, but a friendly one, which drew Tina and me into their confidences.

"Clara was telling me," Emilia said, walking towards us, "that she remembers the time an elderly lady. . ."

She stopped, and turning to Clara, said, "Was her name Ilena?"

"*Si, Si,*" Clara said.

"What was I saying? Oh, yes. Every afternoon, after her husband died, Signora Ilena, dressed in black from head to toe with a dark scarf tied around her chin, came and sat on a chair by her husband's tomb till the cemetery closed." Emilia paused, glanced at the man who was entering the cemetery, then continued.

"Ilena talked to the picture of her deceased husband all afternoon as if it were the most natural thing to do."

"Do you remember, Emilia, how the custodian of the cemetery began to worry?" Clara added.

Tina and I laughed in compliance, but the story did not end there. Clara went on to say that people in Murano wondered if Signora Ilena had gone mad. Some people suggested calling the priest; some suggested talking to her family. The custodian decided to listen to the woman's private conversation.

"Tony, *ti sta ben*?" He heard her say. "Tony, are you fine? Good, I am fine too. Stay there. You have no idea how happy I am without you."

We laughed.

It felt strange to hear people laugh and tell stories about the dead because at age twelve, just thinking about the possibility of Papa and Mama dying put me into a crying frenzy.

I also remember the time I walked all over the cemetery with Mama to bring flowers to our deceased grandparents and all our great aunts who had lived saint-like lives. As we walked, Mama spied her friend.

"How long has it been, Malia?" Mama said, "It seems impossible that he has been gone all of these years."

"Do you remember how good he was? I do not know how I've made it without him. He was a saint of a man!" Malia whispered as she moved her head back and forth, her eyes misty.

After we walked away from Malia, Mama told me that one summer, while Malia was on vacation in the mountains, her husband "went" with the next-door neighbor, their small factory's bookkeeper. No one would have known about it, but the bookkeeper became pregnant. When Malia came back from vacation, the bookkeeper asked if she could still do their accounting. Mama said she felt bad for Malia because she was a decent woman who truly loved her husband. She said it was a good thing Malia could love and remember her husband for his good qualities and for the good times they had together, instead of harboring resentment.

I was not sure I agreed with Mama, and when I saw Tina, I talked to her about it. We decided that we did not know if we could forgive an unfaithful husband or if we could openly proclaim him a saint after his death.

But as Mama always said at the end of a story, "We cannot judge other people's decisions because a lot depends on the person and on the circumstances."

The day we saw Ilda, another one of Mama's friends, she was kneeling by her husband's tomb, shining it at a frenetic pace. She moved her right arm up and down the flat base of the granite tomb with a large old wool sweater, which she used as a rag. She moved her hand in a circular motion to make sure there were no imperfections. As she performed her task, eyes level with the granite slab, she lowered her head to see if she had done a perfect job. She blew her breath on several spots and went over them with the wool rag many times before she was satisfied.

"Wait," Mama said, "let me say hi to Ilda."

Ilda must have heard her because she looked up.

"Teresa," she said to Mama. "You see, this son of a bitch left me."

Ilda was never good at refining her speech. That was the way she talked even when she came over to our house for a visit. When she left the house, Mama always mentioned that we must never talk like Ilda.

That day at the cemetery Ilda spat out a hundred words a minute, telling Mama and me how sad she was that "he" had left her and what a "dickhead" he was for doing that.

Gelmina said it must have been Ilda's remorse working through her busy arms and hands because when her husband was alive she cursed him every minute of the day and night for more than thirty-five years.

As Mama talked to Signora Ilda, I stood behind her, embarrassed, not knowing whether to hide or to say hello. I could not believe that Signora Ilda already forgot the time when Tina and I walked through *Fondamenta dei Vetrai* by her house on the way to meet our friends at the church field, and Signora Ilda was outside leaning against the wall by her front door.

"*Buon giorno* Signora Ilda," we said.

"Are you looking for those boys?" Signora Ilda startled us. "If you walk faster you can catch up with them. They just crossed the bridge."

Tina and I were shocked that she read so much into our innocent walk, and that she assumed we were running after the boys as if we had a note on our foreheads that said, "Looking for the boys."

But that was not all that surprised us that day.

"It's so nice to see young people in love," Signora Ilda said with a nostalgic look on her face. "I wish I had never married my husband." She did not say the word husband. She used a different appellation.

"Look at me. Old as I am, I still wish I had married my first love."

Tina squeezed my arm. We stared at Ilda, at her bright blue eyes, her thin lips cutting across her lower cheeks like a paper slash, her faded blond hair, her body broader than taller, forty pounds overweight, looking at us with envy. Signora Ilda told us about the time she had a terrible fight with her boyfriend. How he left and never came back. She waited for him for two years, and when he didn't show up, she married "that old man." Ilda interrupted her story to fill us in on the character and disposition of her husband and his respected family. She talked about his cantankerous disposition and how she could never make him happy no matter what she did.

She paused for a few seconds, looked at us with teary eyes, and said, "He came back. My first love came back to my house the morning of the wedding and wanted to talk to me."

Signora Ilda lowered her eyes, fidgeted with the edge of her belt and said, "He wanted me to cancel my wedding. I was in my bedroom in my white dress and veil, and he demanded to talk to me, but my father chased him out of the house. I found out after my wedding that he had been there."

I was not sure I wanted Signora Ilda to tell us the rest of the story, but she continued. "For the last thirty-five years I have dreamed of him. At times, I feel he is in bed right next to me, touching me, caressing me, kissing me with passion. Instead, when I open my eyes I find that son of a bitch." She sighed and added, "What can I do, *beie signorine*! I didn't mean to tell you this. Anyway, it's water under the bridge."

Tina and I had no idea people actually married without being in love. We were shocked at what Signora Ilda said, however, we were not shocked that she took us into her confidence because that is what people did if you had two ears to listen.

But it did surprise me when I found out that every single day at ten o'clock in the morning, after she did her housework, Signora Ilda went to the cemetery armed with wax, several woolen rags, a brush, and cleaned her old man's marble stone to a shiny luster.

This is when Tina and I realized that the cemetery was a very strange place, and that once inside, people suffered from amnesia.

Later on Mama said that Signora Ilda was lonely, that loneliness is a terrible thing that breaks people's hearts, that makes people wish they were dead, too. Loneliness was when people heard the howling of the wind and felt the fog in their hearts.

In Murano, the fog came in the fall and lasted all winter long. On certain days, you couldn't even see the tips of your shoes. It was a scary feeling to be walking on the streets, knowing that there were other people around, but all you saw were ghostly figures in the distance. It was even more scary to walk in the fog at night for it felt like you were the only person on the face of the earth.

For the most part, I perceived the inside of the cemetery as a place of repose and rest. A place of solace, not sadness or sorrow, but one of comfort where people came to terms with the mystery of death, with their loved ones, and yes, even with the ones they had not loved so much.

The Infirmary

I stayed in bed with a high fever for a whole week, and so did Gelmina, Margherita, and Giuliana. Mama had transformed the second bedroom into a hospital ward so we could keep each other company. Half of the time we slept, the other half we talked, teased, and begged Gelmina to tell us stories.

As the fever persisted, Mamma called the doctor. He came to the house several times. Giuliana's and Margherita's mouths and tongues had blistered from the high fever. Mama spoon-fed them, as they could not eat from the pain. She sat by their bedsides, making sure she did not touch the sore areas around their mouths. She prepared for them unsalted mashed potatoes, vegetables, lukewarm chicken broth, the yoke of a soft-boiled egg and baked apples.

Papa, who oversaw the menu, praised Mama for her indefatigable disposition, her resilience, her blind loyalty, and her commitment to the family. He always told us that Mama was like the Goddess Minerva. He trusted her wisdom implicitly, for Mama was gifted with the type of wisdom one does not learn, but that which is imprinted at birth within one's soul, just like Antonio's. She was Papa's companion, his friend, his mentor, and his adviser. She was his soul-mate: the best girl in Murano.

Mama worked from early morning to late into the night like a proud and ambitious leader fighting to win a war. Every day, she cooked, cleaned, washed the clothes, and all of the floors in the house with Gelmina's help. She took apart and reassembled old coats, shirts, dresses and slacks with Aunt Susi's help. Without ever uttering a single word of complaint, she orchestrated and juggled the family through life like a magician. As Papa skillfully made us see what was not there with his magic tricks as he made things disappear and appear, Mama made sure everyone in Murano saw what she wanted them to see.

When the doctor came, he prescribed suppositories for Gelmina. To lower our fever and give us strength, he inflicted Margherita, Giuliana and me with shots. Papa paced up and down the corridor, wondering if the doctor should have waited a while longer before shooting the needle into our behinds with the same speed one pokes a piece of roast beef.

"Why can't we have suppositories like Gelmina? Why did you call the doctor? Why can't Papa cure us?"

I missed going to the cemetery with Mama on Monday. Visitors came to the house all week long to ask how we were and to give Mama advice on how to make us feel more comfortable. Everyone had a special method, a medicine, a cream they brought to Mama because they said that if it had worked for their children, it should work for us as well. Tina had visited on Thursday night and thought that I was getting better. She came back on Sunday at one o'clock to see why I had not showed up at the cafè in the morning after church. She talked to me from the bedroom door because Mama said it would be better if we still kept a distance.

Tina stopped at the threshold and smiled at everyone. "Gelmina, how are things going?" she said. "Oh, you are still sick. My sister Elisa is in bed, too."

Tina unbuttoned her checkered coat and began to stroke her rabbit lapel. She had a Twiggy silhouette, not fully developed yet, but graceful and refined. I thought how pretty she looked in the bright orange sweater she had knitted with the help of her mother.

"Look how beautiful Tina looks," Gelmina said.

"Did you go and have your hair done," I asked.

"Do you like it? I thought I would try something different."

Tina moved her head to the side. The sunlight sparkled through her short, silky red hair like a myriad of stars—an agreeable contrast to her blanched skin.

"Did you color your hair?" I said.

"Oh, no!" She glanced at my dull hair, "Mama would not let me. I used henna. I have some more at home that you can try when you feel better."

I nodded. I brushed my curls back and tried to envision how my hair would look with a reddish hue in it.

As Tina talked with Gelmina, I scanned the room. Our bedroom was clean and in order. Earlier, Mama had washed and waxed the floor, dusted all the furniture with the remnant of an old sweater, changed the pillowcases, and folded the sheets she had pressed on top of the blankets. Mama had embroidered a fine, delicate design on the wide hem of each sheet that now lay like an elegant immaculate table runner across each bed.

Margherita, who had been reading the comic book Papa bought for us the previous day, questioned Tina about Elisa.

I wanted to know if Davide had gone to church in the morning, and if he had been at the cafè with Aldo. I wondered if she was going to the movies in the afternoon.

"How are Davide and Aldo doing?" Gelmina said with her usual spunk. "Are they downstairs?"

Tina blushed and hesitated for a moment before she answered.

"No, Gelmina. They are not downstairs. I think they went home." She gave Gelmina a bright smile and a conspicuous glance.

"Is there a party at Renzo's house this afternoon?" I said.

Tina nodded.

"Are you going to the party?"

"I do not know. I would like to," she said. "I wish you were feeling better."

I could not answer her. A few unwelcome tears surfaced. I did not understand why I became so emotional. After all, Gelmina just asked what Davide and Aldo were doing.

The doorbell rang.

"Signora Teresa," Tina said, "Do you want me to open the door?"

Mama appeared from behind the kitchen door, moving like a motorboat at full speed ahead, and said, "No, *bambina.* I'll open it. Thank you."

"Who is it," Mama asked as she pressed her finger on the electric door opener on the wall.

Through the intercom, we heard a mumble, a loud grunt and a voice bellowing,   "Dino."

The Monster

Dino was a monster, or at least we children thought so. He was tall, large, not obese, but an imposing figure with a hump on his back and a distorted face. One side of his cheek protruded upward, and his huge lips hung crooked to one side, causing his speech to slur.

Dino meandered all over Murano, mostly by himself. Children feared him and ran away from him as he approached, screaming in a frenzy, "*Il Mostro, il Mostro.*"

Dino came from a good family. His mother and sister taught him how to read, how to do simple arithmetic, and kept him busy all day with chores. They sent him to the bread store, to the grocery store, to the post office, to the tobacco store, to the fruit vendor. Adults treated him with respect because there was an unwritten law in Murano which decreed that no matter what you did or said, or what misfortune fell upon you during your lifetime, you were an intrinsic part of the community. Out of respect for your family, they accepted you or your deeds unconditionally—of course after having talked about you for several days.

Even though Mama had explained to us children that Dino was a good and gentle man, when on my own, I avoided him. I walked on the far edge of the *fondamenta* or quickly stepped over the bridge across the canal from where he stood. In spite of my precautions, every time I turned around, Dino appeared.

Like the day Mama took me to the doctor in Venice because my heart had been racing fast, and its palpitations gave way to her concern. Perhaps my heart raced because at twelve I was in love for the first time, or because

I drank too many espresso coffees. It didn't matter. Mama decided to take me to a heart specialist.

On a Tuesday afternoon, Mama and I walked to the *Colonna* and caught the three o'clock boat to Venice. When the boat arrived, I trailed behind Mama down the few steps. We sat next to the door, and to my horror, Dino and his sister sat across from us.

Dino greeted us, looked around at the other passengers, one by one, then lowered his head and became silent.

"*Buon giorno*, Signora Mirna," Mama said, smiling at Dino's sister.

Signora Mirna answered with, "Is this your daughter, Anna? *Che bella signorina!*"

It did not surprise me that the nice lady knew my name. It would not have surprised me if she had known what doctor I was going to see and at what time I had the appointment. Or which friends I had met in the morning, and who I was going to meet in the afternoon. She seemed to be a very fine lady who knew everything about our family down to our first ancestor.

The lady told us that when she was a little girl, she used to see my grandmother at the fruit vendor every Friday. She told Mama how much she admired my grandmother, and how she noticed that my grandmother always bought the biggest and best oranges, apples and other seasonal fruits. The fine lady did not have to tell me that—Mama did it as well.

Like her mother before her, Mama bought the biggest and the best fruit and gave each of us children a fraction of it after dinner. The slice came with an explanation, of course. As Mama sliced the fruit, she remarked about the rich people who bought the smallest apples, like ping-pong balls, for their families.

"All core and seeds, and no pulp," Mama said.

Deep down I wished my grandmother had bought the smallest fruits. After all, as far as I could tell, according to Murano standards, my grandmother was rich. And I would have liked for once in my whole life to have a whole apple without first having to dissect it into twenty small parts. I did not feel the need to always share it with my five siblings, plus Gelmina, Mama and Papa. For once, I wanted to dig my entire row of front teeth into the pulp of a whole apple. I wanted to eat, like my friend Arianna did, the entire apple.

Mama could not be persuaded. She was adamant about carrying on with the family traditions. On rare occasions, she also bought the strongest fabric to make our clothes so they would last forever. They could be reversed, sewed into brand new ones and passed down to each of my siblings year after year. On occasion, Mama told us that during the Christmas holidays her Mama and Papa took the whole family to Venice and bought them each a pair of quality winter shoes and the best quality clothes—clothes that lasted a lifetime. Mama did not have to tell me what her own shoes must have looked like because I was sure I was wearing a pair exactly like my grandmother used to buy for her. They resembled more a T34 Russian World War II tank than a pair of shoes. The bottom, a thick, brown rubber sole with a tire like design, could withstand a very, very wet and icy winter. The leather lining on the inside could prevent our feet from getting wet. The square, pointed top adorned with double rows of heavy stitches carried out around the whole shoe, emphasized its bulky shape even more. I knew that like Mama, grandmother meant well, but I wanted shoes like my best friend, Tina.

Tina's mother and father took her and her siblings to Venice, as well, during the Christmas holidays, but the children were allowed to pick the shoes they wanted. Tina always came back home smiling, while I returned home from shopping with Mama mad.

Tina's shoes were not lined in leather and had a round shape with a *decolté* cut in the front and a black shiny bow on the top. Her feet froze during the winter months, but her shoes looked trendy. Tina must have felt sorry for me because most of the time when we met, right in the middle of the *fondamenta,* we would exchange shoes. I ended up going home with Tina's shoes and by the end of the day, if the temperature was below zero, I would come down with a slight case of frostbite which kept me in agony during the night as my feet swelled, itched and ached.

Mama did not relent. She was proud she bought shoes for us that kept our feet dry and warm just like her Papa and Mama had done for her. It was useless for me to cry because my pragmatic Mama always said that if I kept up the whining, she would give me something to really whine about. She meant it, too. Mama was loving and caring, but she was the disciplinarian in the family and had within the core of her soul her own solid ideas about discipline that her mother and father had instilled in her.

As I smiled politely and listened to Mama and Signora Mirna's conversation, I glanced at Dino, his head bent to one side, eyes squinting, staring across the aisle at the lady sitting with her daughter. It was impossible not to look at Dino now because he began to mumble. I couldn't decide if the various noises were part of his natural process of thinking, or if they were a prelude to an eruption. His sister must have heard him as well. She stopped talking to Mama, put a hand on Dino's legs and gave him a gentle shake.

"Dino, Dino," she said. "What are you doing? Look at me. Dino, Dino."

Dino was not listening. He had his own agenda in mind because after his sister uttered the second pair of Dinos, he got up. With an icy stare at the lady across the aisle, he extended his right arm, moved it back and forth and sideways like a pendulum.

He exerted himself to pronounce the words clearly and shouted, "Family should never. . ." He paused for a second as he bent his body forwards, and continued. "Never fight over money. Never fight over inheritance."

He sat down again, slapped his arm on his leg, turned to face Mama and me, and lowered his head.

Poor Dino. Poor sister. Poor lady across the aisle. For a moment I thought the veins in Dino's neck would explode.

After Dino's burst of morality, all I could hear was the boat's engine, and my own heartbeat.

For many days afterward, people walked through the *fondamente* in Murano saying, "Did you hear what Dino said to that lady?"

If someone didn't know the "lady," a lengthy explanation followed.

"Yes, you remember the lady who is married to the *pasticcere*, the one who has a shop in *Calle San Giuseppe*, the one who always donates all of the sweet breads to the church on Christmas Eve."

"Oh, you mean Alba. . ."

"No, not Alba, but her sister-in-law."

"Yes, yes, I know who you mean. The lady who lives near Carla, the daughter of the man who has a dog named Luigi."

"No, not the daughter of the man with the dog, but the daughter of the sister of the man with the dog named Luigi."

In the end, people claimed they knew the "lady," and at that point the whole story would be disclosed to the very last detail.

That day on the boat, I did not understand Dino's statement, but Mama explained it to me and to my siblings many times over, to make sure we all understood Dino's message. Mama said that the lady who sat across the aisle from Dino had not talked to her brother since their mother died because the brother did not want to give her half of their parent's inheritance. She said the voices of Murano had speculated the lady was going to take her brother to court.

To make her point, Mama repeated to us that Dino was not as dumb as people thought. She said, "Imagine, to learn a lesson like that from a simple man!"

"Who is it, Mama?" Margherita asked as Mama waited for Dino to come up the stairs.

"It's Dino, I don't know what he wants."

"Dino?" we uttered in unison.

A fatigued, out-of-breath Dino reached the door and handed Mama a piece of yellow-lined paper. I knew he would bow to her and bring his opened right hand to his temple, as in a military salute. He would walk back towards the stairs, wave, and say to her in his abysmal voice, "*Buon Appetito*," as he disappeared down the stairs.

Mama walked towards the bedroom door where everyone's eyes were focused on the piece of paper she held in her hand.

"Oh, it's a note from the Women's Catholic Federation," she said. "They are inviting me to go to their meeting next week."

Papa came out of the bathroom. Surprised to see Tina, he said it was too bad everyone was sick, or he would have suggested that she stay for lunch. He asked her about her father and his business, and said, "I wish your father the best of everything. With four children and all to feed. *Eh, si.* Things are not easy these days."

Tina nodded. Papa repeated that he knew things were hard for everyone, that the economy was not strong, but with God's help, they all would survive one more winter.

He said, "Yes, *bambini*, always put your trust in God."

It was time for Tina to go to eat. She said, *"Arrivederci a tutti,"* and disappeared down the stairs while I slid under the sheet to hide the tears that fell on my cheeks.

God Has a Sense of Humor

All was silent at our house, but for the constant flow of water running from the kitchen sink's faucet where Mama washed the Sunday lunch dishes. Gabri, Antonio, and Pietro had gone to the movies. Papa took a half hour nap, elbows planted on the table, oblivious of the noises Mama made with the pots and pans.

We were resting in the dormitory: not really sleeping, just lying there engrossed in our own thoughts. I imagined Tina having fun with the boys, smacking them on the head when they teased her, punching their arms as they played tag in the church field. I fantasized about the moment I would enter Signora Maria's house on Wednesday afternoon, walk into the back room, sit by Davide and ask how he was, how school was going.

At two o'clock, Mama entered our bedroom and sat down. "I need to rest for a half an hour, or my body will explode." She sighed.

Mama's face looked flushed. She said her body prickled all over, as if a thousand spikes had dug into the surface of her skin. Her right eye twitched, and she saw a glow of flashing yellow lights when she fixed her eyes on something. She wanted to close her eyes for a few seconds and relax. She got up, went back into the kitchen, sat on a chair, folded her arms on each other in front of her on the table, and laid her tired head on them, trying to control her breathing.

Five minutes later, the doorbell rang.

Dring-g-g, Dring-g-g, Dring-g-g. Three rings, and Mama knew who it was. She did not have to glance outside to know Aunt Claretta was there.

Mama liked Aunt Claretta because she felt the same way about family as Mama and Papa did.

I, too, loved Aunt Claretta.

Mama said she did not have a mean bone in her body. I understood from the few brief conversations I heard over the years, that Aunt Claretta had had a fight with Uncle Paolo's wife and had not talked to her for fifteen years. But I had never noticed anything unusual about their behavior. Every year, they all showed up at our house during the holidays. Uncle Paolo and Aunt Lora sat on one side of the table, Aunt Claretta on the other. They all talked with each other using Papa as a referee. They bounced their words back and forth with dexterity. After dinner, Uncle Paolo took the time to sit next to his sister Claretta and talk to her, and Aunt Lora chatted with cousin Silvana, Aunt Claretta's daughter, and laughed at Silvana's jokes.

Gelmina, from her bed, called, "Signora Teresa, I'll open the door." But Mama's body had sprinted up as usual, and she opened the door before we could shout from our bedroom, "Mama, Aunt Claretta is here."

Aunt Claretta came up the steps.

"Hi, Teresa," she said as they kissed each other on the cheeks.

"Are you all right?" Aunt Claretta said as she scrutinized Mama's face.

"Come in. I'm just tired," Mama said.

"Is Nico sleeping? And the children, are they still in bed? Let me visit with them. You go and sit in the kitchen. Go, go and rest."

Aunt Claretta pushed Mama towards the kitchen door, then, came into our bedroom. She said hi to Gelmina, walked to the side of each bed, kissed us on the cheeks, and like every Sunday, she handed us the fifteen lire to go to the movies. Displaying a radiant smile, Aunt Claretta pulled up a chair and sat by the foot of my bed.

"How are you feeling," she asked everyone.

"We are fine, *Zia*. Mama said that tomorrow we'll get up and Wednesday we'll go back to school."

"*Bravi. Bravi*," she said as she complimented us on how well we looked. She nodded her head in assent, looking at each of us. With hands locked into each other in her lap, she rotated her thumbs as she waited for Margherita and me to ask her to tell us a story.

"*Zia* Claretta, tell us the story about Papa."

"You want that one? I've told it to you so many times."

"Aunt Claretta, we like it. Please, Please," we said.

Resigned, Aunt Claretta, all pretty in her tight, narrow tweed skirt and her pale blue woolen sweater, dolled up as if she were going to the theater, high heels and all, began to recount the story she herself had titled, "God Has a Sense of Humor."

We propped ourselves up in bed and digested every word Aunt Claretta uttered. At times, we tried to anticipate what she was going to say next because Aunt Claretta never changed a word, a comma, or forgot one single detail.

Aunt Claretta began her story, almost whispering. Sometimes, her voice exploded into laughter, or pretend sobs. She mimicked the characters with all the nuances the story required to be effective. She impersonated the characters, bringing them alive, as if they had been right there in our bedroom.

"One day," she began, "when I arrived home, my Mama, your *Nonna*, was laughing with gusto by the kitchen sink. She laughed, laughed, and laughed, all happy as she repeated, 'God sure has the best sense of humor. . .Ha ha ha.'"

"What, tell me, come on, Mama, tell me," Aunt Claretta asked her Mama.

Aunt Claretta said that *Nonna* kept on laughing. That was how *Nonna* always acted when an incident of long ago took a somewhat ironic turn. That is what she did when something unexpected happened in her family.

"*Si, bambini,*" Aunt Claretta said, " like your *Nonna* always said, even after many years, God has a way to teach us, to humble us."

Margherita, Giuliana, Gelmina and I mimicked her mouthing her words. We knew what she meant. The whole family knew why our *Nonna* had jumped up and down, laughing and repeating that God for sure had a sense of humor. *Nonna* had never forgotten what Papa's teacher, Signor Gabini, had said about Papa when she went to school to inquire about his progress.

Aunt Claretta continued her story by telling us that when our Papa was six years old, *Nonna* went for a school conference with his first grade teacher, Signor Gabini. At home, after her conference, tears poured out of *Nonna*'s eyes, falling on the kitchen table. Uncle Paolo and Aunt Claretta, who sat across from *Nonna*, stared at her in disbelief. The other uncles, who were younger, cried in solidarity as they hugged *Nonna*'s body. Looking at Aunt

Claretta behind a veil of tears, as she wiped her eyes and the table with the black sleeve of her housedress, *Nonna* mumbled, "It's. . .It's. . .It's about Signor Gabini. This morning, he told me Nico is stupid."

"Your son is stupid, stupid, stupid," Signor Gabini had said to *Nonna* who was standing across from his desk in the empty classroom. Bewildered from such utterances, *Nonna*'s eyes began to sting.

"Nico is a little boy, a very active little boy." *Nonna* replied in a faint whisper.

"Ohhh, no," Signor Gabini went on, "it's not that."

Signor Gabini stared at her as if he wanted to shatter her dark shiny pupils with his words.

"Nico is the stupidest child I have ever encountered in my career as a teacher. He'll never amount to anything," he declared with resolution.

Aunt Claretta stopped to let us digest what she had just said. She nodded, and went on to say that she knew *Nonna* could not say one more word to Signor Gambini after his declaration. When *Nonna* walked out of the classroom, she bumped into Uncle Paolo's teacher, Signor Pasto. He listened to *Nonna*'s story, and seeing her distress, he placed his arm on her shoulder and said, "Signora Marchini, why are you crying? Imagine, saying a thing like that about a six year old child. Do not pay attention to what he said. Nico is going to be fine. He is just very active."

"Signor Gabini's children are still infants," he added as if he were talking to himself. "I think he is in for a rude awakening."

It meant a lot to *Nonna* to talk to Signor Pasto, to hear his kind words before she left the school and headed for home.

Aunt Claretta told us that *Nonna* said hello to a lot of people on the way home, but she couldn't remember seeing any of them because her eyes were draped with sad tears, and the words, "Stupid, stupid, stupid. . .the stupidest child," reverberated in her head like a chant.

The news of what happened to *Nonna* did not faze Grandfather. When he came home in the evening, Aunt Claretta gave her account of the story, which was much more dramatic than *Nonna*'s.

"Do you see," Grandfather said to *Nonna,* "even Signor Pasto said not to pay attention to that man." Then he added, "We have to feel sorry for people like that. They have no compassion and no love in their hearts."

Grandfather took a few steps closer to *Nonna*, embraced her waist with both of his arms, swayed her back and forth for a few seconds and ended the conversation, whispering, "Do not worry Alba, forget all about it."

Grandfather was as good as my Papa in teaching people about love. When Grandfather saw Signor Gabini on the *fondamenta*, he waved his arm in the air and called, "Signor Gabini, how are you? How is your family? I saw your wife with the three girls yesterday. *Son belle!*"

Turning to Aunt Claretta he said, "He has a lot to learn about life."

When Nonna saw Signor Gabini, she said a very dry *buon giorno*, more with her head than with her mouth, and went about her business.

At this point of the story, Aunt Claretta stopped. She looked around the room at us, fixed her skirt, her hair, and waited.

"Aunty, come on, this is the best part of the story," we said in unison.

"Calm down. Calm down," she said, bringing her right hand up and down, caressing the open air, as if she were the maestro of a chorus instructing the musicians to tone down their pitch.

"And do you know what?" she added. "Seventeen years later, *Nonna* felt victorious because Signor Gabini's eldest daughter fell in love with your Papa."

"And Signor Gabini invited Papa over to his house for dinner," we sang out.

"Exactly," Aunt Claretta said. "Seventeen years later, Signor Gabini's eldest daughter fell in love with your Papa."

"And do you know what else?" Aunt Claretta said, raising her arms, stretching them high, holding the index and medium fingers apart as a sign of victory, and stamping her pumps on the floor.

"She followed Papa around like a duck," we answered.

A Duck. Aunt Claretta called Signor Gabini's daughter a duck because she followed Papa around Murano for a whole year, just like a little duck.

Every time Aunt Claretta saw Papa in Murano, the duck as well was spotted in the vicinity.

Gelmina laughed.

Aunt Claretta sounded just like Gelmina when she told stories and identified people by calling them all kinds of names.

I thought of what Mama always said to Gelmina. "Gelmina, why do you label people? Why can't you just call them by their names?"

It was no use. Gelmina couldn't help it. Gelmina, always playful, made fun of everybody. And Mama, like a sergeant, could not find humor in Gelmina's jokes. Perhaps Gelmina wanted to amuse us children, or to embellish her life with a little humor, but Mama did not appreciate it.

Mama scolded Gelmina when she told us to go and kick the wooden door of the old man who lived by the bridge in *fondamenta Venier* so that he and his dog would bark as we ran away.

We loved Gelmina and her mischievous soul, and the stories she made up sometimes before we went to sleep.

When we cajoled Gelmina into telling us a story, our ears would perk up. Gelmina told and retold certain events or gossip about the neighbor, or about Dino, or about Gabri's imaginary boyfriend who supposedly, one day, came to the house looking for her and then jumped out of the window when he heard Mama approach the entrance door. He was now injured for life, meandering the streets of Murano at night, amidst the thick fog, with only one arm and one leg. He had no teeth and a patch on one eye.

Aunt Claretta went on to explain that it was sort of a small victory for our *Nonna* when Signor Gabini invited Papa to his house. But she always emphasized that the most important thing to remember was that the real victory for *Nonna* had been watching Papa grow up to become a very fine person, like Grandfather.

The afternoon went by fast. Gabri came in with her friend Norma, Antonio with his three friends from the Boy Scouts, and Pietro with Tina's brother. They sat around the kitchen table together with Mama and Aunt Claretta and played a few games of Bingo. Papa, in the living room, with the door shut tight, read in his favorite chair by the glass lamp, the history of the formation of Italy, about *La Giovane Italia*, Mazzini, and Cavour in the school-book Margherita lent him.

Between Aunt Claretta's story, the doorbell ringing as people came and went throughout the afternoon, evening fell early now that winter was looming ahead. Meanwhile, Gelmina, Margherita, Giuliana and I took turns going to the bathroom, switching on the lights in the corridor so that we could peer through the glass door that separated the entrance hall from the kitchen.

Every light in the house emanated a warm glow, a feeling of togetherness. Outside, one could see the dizzy distant glow of the streetlights transpiring amidst a thick blanket of fog. The fog began hovering throughout, undeterred. It crept though the lagoon, invaded the street, inch by inch, and enveloped the old tiled roofs. It fabricated a gray, opaque foamy wall, the type of thick fog that gave you the sensation of stepping through a slate of menacing clouds. You knew you were touching the ground, merely because you could still feel the hard cobblestones under your feet.

That Sunday, after all the guests left, around eight o'clock, we went into the kitchen to eat dinner. Even though our fevers had gone down, we retired to our beds soon afterwards.

I looked with anticipation to Wednesday, when I would meet Tina at the *Ponte Lungo*, walk to the boat station, and perhaps, catch a glimpse of Davide before school. In the meantime, I fancied myself entering Signora Maria's house on Wednesday afternoon, walking past the dining room and the kitchen, to the very last room where all of the tables were set out for the students, and sitting in the very last empty place next to Davide.

The Massoni Theater

On Wednesday, I met Tina at the *Ponte Lungo*. We ran to the *Colonna* trying to catch the seven-thirty boat. Carrying our books, panting, we passed some of our friends, said a furtive, "hello," and kept on running. However, when we got to the *Colonna*, we saw the tail-end of the seven-thirty boat leaving the station. We started laughing like two silly girls. We wiped the sweat from our faces and approached the station.

"Your hair is kinky," Tina said. To allay any unpleasantness, she reassured me that my green eyes really shone so much more when my curly hair framed my face.

"I hate my curly hair. I got up early and stretched my hair for half an hour with the iron my Aunt Susi lent me."

I raised my shoulders as if to say, it's no use, the moisture makes my hair curly. I said, "Did you say my teeth sparkle, too, when my hair kinks?"

We laughed again. It felt good to be with Tina. Most of all I wanted to find out about the previous Sunday afternoon because Tina had a suspicious twinkle in her eyes.

When we arrived in Venice, we took a secondary route to school, a deserted one so that we could talk. As we walked arm in arm, I listened to Tina's account of her Sunday with Davide.

"After lunch I met with Vana at the *Ponte Lungo*." Tina said.

She and Vana, a new friend whose family had just moved to our island, decided to go to the Massoni Theater to see a movie starring Elvis Presley. Tina casually mentioned that she knew the boys were going to be there. I was rather surprised Tina went to the Massoni as she knew that whoever went to the Massoni Theater was up to no good. And I knew it, too. For if you went there, you sat in the last few rows, and you did things you would not have done in the open air: kissed and smoked.

"I know what you want to say," Tina said. "I know my Mama and your Mama do not allow us to go there because the devil hides under the red chairs."

Tina and I rolled our eyes, laughing.

"Yes, I went," she said.

I couldn't believe that Sunday afternoon, while I lay in bed listening to Aunt Claretta's story, Tina had gone to the Massoni.

"What happened," I said. "Tell me, tell me," I repeated with impatience, wanting to know her secret.

We stopped. Tina leaned against a withered hump of plaster on one of the walls along the way and looked at me. Her expression spoke of jitters. Her skinny legs lurched back and forth, unable to stand still, and her hand twirled her small crochet wallet non-stop.

Tina whispered all the particulars of her first kiss with Davide.

I was shaken and jealous. But I said nothing to her. Instead, I suppressed my tears. I was also envious she had had the courage to go to the Massoni. Tina understood and together, we planned my first visit to the Massoni.

All week long, we plotted how I would go to the Massoni. What I would say to Mama on Sunday after lunch, without raising any suspicion when it was time to say goodbye and walk out of the house. Laughing ourselves silly, Tina and I practiced the tone I would use. We asked each other every question we could think of that Mama might ask before I left the house.

On that same Wednesday, after lunch, when I arrived at Signora Maria's house, after school, she welcomed me as if I had been the prodigal son coming home after a long absence. Even her old, nonchalant Golden Retriever, who usually lay in the corner of the living room watching the students come and go, stood up when I entered the room, ears fanned, eyes focused on me as if I were a walking bone.

The treble in Signora Maria's voice high above the perennial chaos that reigned within the two rooms, marked by the comment that I looked pale, made me uncomfortable. The moment I entered the room, I was aware of everyone looking at me. I wished my body had metamorphosed into a nacreous substance, instead of the feeble mollusk I felt it was transforming into.

"Anna, how are you? You look so pale. Come, come. . ." Signora Maria said as she embraced me. She pointed to the empty seat right in front of Davide, and said, "Davide was saving that place for you."

My face moved in Davide's direction. I tipped my body forward, lifted one leg, then the other, over the bench in the empty space, praying that no one would notice my flushed face. I said hello to everyone, and sat, pretending to busy myself with my books in order to gain my self composure before anyone pointed out the obvious and said, "*Sembri un peperone rosso.*"

No one really said that I looked like a red pepper, but when I lifted my eyes and looked beyond Davide's head, I saw Aldo at the next table with his insolent little smile, ready to tease me. As he stroked his cheeks with his fingers, he mouthed, "How red!" and laughing, he mumbled something I could not comprehend. Then, he continued to talk to Sele who was seated next to him.

I finally looked at Davide and smiled.

"I heard you went to the Massoni Theater with Tina last Sunday," I heard my voice saying.

I felt as if my throat had been galvanized by some unforeseen forces. I blushed again. I was not really sure I wanted him to respond.

Davide looked at me for a few seconds but ignored my remark.

"I wrote a poem. Would you like to read it?" he said.

For a moment our eyes locked, and I felt a spark flying between us. It was a feeling I could not explain. It made no sense at all. But it remained within me for the remainder of the week, and it gave me the necessary fuel to plan my escapade to the Massoni.

"Do you want me to read it to you," Davide persisted. He took a lined, folded piece of paper out of his pocket and placed it in front of me.

Davide's poem, several stanzas in couplets, was about a beautiful young woman with long blond hair who walked towards her lover in a pastoral setting by a lake. He read the poem with a lot of feeling, at times, pausing to emphasize his words. When he read about the gorgeous young woman walking towards her lover, I had to exert all my will power not to show emotion. As I tried to guess who the young girl was, disappointed that the girl in his poem did not have dark, curly hair, when Davide's voice stopped, I said, "Do I know the girl?"

"No, I made her up."

"Oh, I see. The girl of your dreams," I said.

He did not answer but nodded his head with vehemence. He folded his poem and placed it in his pants' pocket.

For the rest of the afternoon, I tried to concentrate on my homework, but my thoughts kept wandering back to the Massoni.

The following Sunday, I wore my old, "new" navy blue pleated skirt a bit too long over my knees, a white cotton blouse, and my sister Margherita's shiny blue shoes. After lunch, I spread a light layer of Gabri's make-up on my rosy cheeks, and applied clear lip-gloss. I straightened my hair, teased it a little on the top for fullness, parted it on the side, curled it under, fixed my bangs away from my forehead to make my face appear longer, and said goodbye to Mama from the entrance hall.

"Where are you going," Mama asked from the Kitchen.

"I'm going to the movies with Tina," I yelled back.

You would think that instead of listening to what I said, Mama had read my mind. You would think she didn't trust me, that it didn't matter what I said because what she heard was what she imagined I said.

In a crystal clear tone, she asked, "You are not going to the Massoni Theater, are you."

Trying to control my voice, I answered, "*Ma no*, Mama, don't worry."

When I was younger, I could never figure out how Mama found out everything I did. How she could repeat at any given moment every little detail of my teenage private life even before I had time to realize what had happened, myself. Utterly surprised at how Mama always knew, at how the whole island knew everything about me, like a detective I questioned everyone with, "Who told you."

On the island, people took a fragment of your life and made it their own when there was not enough excitement in theirs. Of course, I made my contribution and gave people plenty to talk about.

Even though Mama, who was a very religious woman, strictly forbade us to set foot in the Massoni because the devil dwelled under the red chairs, I resolved to go.

For days afterwards, I tried to figure out how Mama discovered that I had gone to the Massoni even before I returned home.

Mama knew human nature.

Perhaps Father Matteo's sermon about how God knows in advance every decision we are going to make, even though He gives us a free choice, had something to do with it.

Father Matteo said to all of his parishioners as if it were the most natural thing to understand, convinced that his was an axiomatic explanation, "God gives us the choice to decide if we want to be good or bad, but he knows in advance how we are going to behave."

That was the part I could not understand. No matter how many times I thought about it, no matter how many questions I asked on the subject, I could never understand how people were free to choose if God already knew how they were going to behave.

Several questions mulled in my mind: How can I be good, if God already knows that I'm going to be bad? How could I not go to the Massoni if Mama already knew I was going?

I guess Mama understood what I didn't about God and free choices because even if Father Matteo did not make his point clear, having six children must have enlightened her.

Mama must have known how the natural disposition of men plays an intrinsic part in the decisions they make. She must have known why the priest kept on hammering that statement into our innocent heads, and why he kept on repeating the free choice sermon to us, even though he knew we did not get it.

With all of his rhetorical training, Father Matteo could have said, "Let's just suppose that you are the fathers and mothers of two children, Adam and Eve. Adam is a happy child. He does what you ask and listens to everything you say. Eve, on the other hand, is a bit defiant, adventurous, and somewhat independent. One Sunday, Adam and Eve go out to meet their friends. Before they leave their house, you, as their parent, give them permission to go to the church theater, but not to the Massoni. Because you know your two children's nature, you also know in advance exactly which child is going to mind and which one is going to disobey you."

Father Matteo could have paused for a second to give us time to digest the explanation, then he could have said, "Do you see how you, the parents, gave Adam and Eve free choice?"

Yes, for sure, we would have understood that. It seemed like a very simple and clear explanation, which the priest, not having children of his own, never gave us, and which Mama kept to herself.

Like Eve would have done, I made my free choice and went to the Massoni with Vana. And Mama, like God, knew it.

It was not really my fault if I went to the Massoni to see a double feature. It was not Tina's fault because she could not go that day. It was simply love's fault.

On the way to the movies, I made sure I looked inconspicuous. I knew that if I made the wrong move, and instead of turning right I turned left, people would have suspected my whereabouts. That is why I first walked in the opposite direction from the Massoni. Sure, I met a few people on the way, but no one I knew well. As I walked, I scanned all the windows to see if anyone was hanging his head out. I checked to see if anyone I knew was scouting for something to tell Mama.

I was careful because I did not want people to "innocently" approach Mama and say, "Signora Teresa, I saw your daughter Anna go by my house on Sunday at two o'clock. She is such a nice young lady."

It would have only taken that little bit of information to give away my whereabouts. But I was on safe ground in that respect because at that particular time people were taking their Sunday afternoon naps, and no one was concerned which theater I was going to, except Mama.

I passed the church theater. No one was outside. I turned towards *Ponte delle Terese*, made a left, and another left. I went by Aunt Lidia and Uncle Rino's house. I walked against the wall so that if Aunt Lidia was washing the dishes instead of taking a nap, she would not see me. I turned right at the next corner, and another swift right into the Massoni.

Vana was in the lobby waiting for me.

"Hurry, the movie has already started," she said.

We pulled aside the red curtains. It was dark, so we stopped to adjust our eyes.

Davide and Aldo saw us.

"Anna, Vana, come sit here," Davide said.

I went in first, so I sat next to Davide.

I watched the movie, but did not see it. Even in the dark, with my peripheral vision, I was aware of every movement Davide made. From time to time he whispered something which I did not understand. Even though I loved Elvis' movies, I could not follow the simple plot. At the precise moment Elvis played and sang his loudest song, Davide, with one decisive movement, put an arm around me and began to stroke my shoulder.

As the movie played on, he leaned his body towards me. He kissed me on the cheek first, then on the mouth.

My heart stopped; my head began to spin. I felt confused and guilty. As soon as the movie was over, I ran to Aunt Susi's house to hide from Mama for the rest of the afternoon.

My pride was shattered later in the afternoon by my brother Antonio who had not been at the Massoni, but had been told by some busybody, that as Davide kissed me, he, as well, turned around and kissed Amelia. I could see that from my brother's stand-point, the picture did not appear romantic at all.

Mama said nothing when I returned home. It was obvious that she already knew every detail of my Sunday afternoon at the Massoni. Mama spoke not a word to me that evening, except for one short sentence during dinner that was directed to all of us children.

"*Bambini*, I want you to remember that the devil makes the pans but always forgets to make the lids."

Gelmina turned to me and said, "*Eh, si, Annetta mia*. Remember that particular."

Saying that, Mama and Gelmina got up to clear the table.

Just Friends

The next day, I avoided Davide. I met with Tina in the morning, and late in the afternoon we went to the cemetery and talked. Tina listened to my confused thoughts that bounced around in my head like tumultuous waves. Like a good friend, she allowed me to sort things out, occasionally steering the conversation with her pragmatic reasoning so that I would not drown in my own sorrows. I told Tina that I wanted to see Davide, but I still felt embarrassed that he had kissed me as well as Amelia during the intermission. At least that is what Antonio told me, and I believed my brother.

All week, I tried to sort out my feelings, hoping my embarrassment would ease. During that week, I went to Signora Maria's house right after lunch, but left before Davide arrived and made the excuse I had to help Papa at the mirror factory.

Yes, no; yes, no; yes and no. I wanted to talk to Davide. No, I did not want to talk to him until at least my cheeks stopped flaring up every time I thought of our first kiss. I always felt better after I expressed my sentiments to Tina and she made fun of our behavior the way only Tina could. The more I shared my thoughts with her, the better I felt.

A week later, one early evening, after I finished helping Papa, while Tina and I walked around Murano in the fog, our skinny legs took us right past Davide's uncle's grocery store where Davide was lending a helping hand. He came out with a handful of candies, and placed them in the palm of our gloved hands.

"Here, take them," he said.

"But, we do not have any money," I said.

"Do not worry. It's on me."

It felt good to smile. There was no need for me to act morose. It was not part of my personality to sulk, anyway. It was better to be his friend, just like Tina's grandmother had said, to have fun, to talk, to meet at the church ground, sit under the portico, lean against the old marble well, and just enjoy each other. While Tina and I walked through Fondamenta Venier, I unwrapped a piece of candy, and arranged my thoughts as if they were the layers of pasta Mama placed in her lasagna pan. The tension I had felt the past week ebbed away. I smiled at Tina, who like a fire cracker, as if she knew something but was not willing to share it, blurted out, "He likes you."

"He does not," I answered back in the same tone.

St. Martin's Day Celebration

Towards the end of November, everyone in Murano was wearing his woolen coat, a scarf wrapped around the neck, a woolen hat, and gloves. You could feel the dampness penetrating the marrow of your bones, freezing it to its very core. In the early morning, before the sun peered through the misty sky, you could spot here and there, in the green-gray water, small pieces of ice floating, scampering within the waves. But life did not slow down in Murano. Not even the frantic pace of the last minute shopping before the stores closed at seven- thirty.

In the early evenings, Tina, Sele, I, and few of our other friends met by the church bridge. Together we walked up and down the Fondamenta dei Vetrai, sure we would see the boys walking across from it. As we walked, we bent our heads a little, pretending to look at something on the pavement. Or we turned to say hello to passersby, while always keeping our focus on the boys. It was just like Mama's friend, Lola, had said, the boys on one side, and the girls on the other, walking, checking each other out.

The evenings were getting darker and colder, and as people stopped next to the windows of the shops on each side of the canal to chat, you could see their breath reflected in the aura of artificial lights. At times, I met Papa on the street and walked home with him, just like I did on the evening of Saint Martin's Day earlier in the month, on the eleventh of November. After attending the evening service, Tina and I left the church and walked ahead toward the Colonna. We spied Papa buying a stock of celery from Renzo's father.

"Eilà, Nico, how can I help you," Renzo's father asked.

"Friend," Papa said, "give me some chestnuts, and a nice stalk of celery. Saint Martin's Day. . .We are going to celebrate tonight."

On Saint Martin's Day, as was the custom, Papa brought home a big stalk of celery and a handful of chestnuts. My younger siblings took turns looking out of the window for Papa's arrival, always around seven-thirty. When they saw him approaching, they crowded at the front door and watched him come up the steps.

"Papa is home!" they shouted from the top of the stairs.

Waving his celery stalk, Papa called out, "Mama, tonight we celebrate. Your brothers are coming. Aunt Susi, Uncle Rino, Aunt Lidia, Uncle Ruggero, Aunt Lina and cousin Adriana are coming after dinner."

"Che festa," he said as he handed the chestnuts to Mama.

In the kitchen, Mama slit a mark through the chestnuts' tough husks and put them on the wood stove in an iron skillet. She covered it and let the chestnuts cook to a tender paste. She placed them in a woolen blanket, so that their soft content continued to cook to the point where they melted in your mouth. Wrapped in the chestnut's scent, Mama washed the dirt off the celery stalks until they were a pale green. She cut and soaked them in the fresh faucet water till the time in which Papa, like a priest during mass who solemnly announces the blessing of the bread and wine, pronounced it was time to eat them.

At nine o'clock, the doorbell rang.

Papa motioned for us to open the door. We children sprang up from our chairs, ran towards the door, pressed the automatic door opener and asked, "Who is it?" and waited.

"Hey, we are here," Uncle Ruggero said.

While we waited, pushing and elbowing each other to be in the front, our guests lugged their bodies up the two steep flights of stairs. They entered the kitchen and commented on how nice and warm the room was. They walked towards the stove where they warmed their hands for a few seconds. They brushed the humidity out of their wet hair as they explained that outside, a veil of fog had strewn over the island, making it impossible to see.

Mama removed the bread-crumbs from the white tablecloth, while Gelmina placed the clean glasses, the silverware, and the dessert dishes in front of everyone. We all huddled around the table as Mama placed on each side a plate of chestnuts, a tall glass with the celery stalks in it, a jug of wine, and a pitcher of fresh water from the faucet in front of Papa. To make the celebration more complete, Aunt Susi took out of her shopping bag a gigantic cookie in the shape of a San Martino on his horse, which she had purchased from Alfio's pasticceria.

Papa was pleased and winked at Mama.

Mama took an empty dish out of the pantry, unwrapped the cookie from the cellophane, and broke it into fifteen pieces.

The feast began.

We peeled the husks off the warm chestnuts, chewed on the crunchy celery sticks, ate with gusto the piece of cookie. For the rest of the evening, we sat around the kitchen table while Uncle Ruggero told us stories about the years he had spent as a soldier fighting in World War II and as a prisoner in an internment camp. Wrapped in Uncle's memories, which became our memories as soon as he relinquished them, we listened.

Uncle Ruggero

U ncle Ruggero never tired of talking about his life in the internment camp in Erfur, Germany, and of his journey back to civilization at the end of the war when his two best friends pushed him in a wheelbarrow for miles because he was too weak to walk. With caution, the three friends, who had no money to eat or travel by train, went from town to town trying to recruit help from the American soldiers they found along the way. During the day, they hid under bridges. At night, they walked. Because of that, it took them months to arrive home. In particular, Uncle remembered, with emotion the moment he arrived at the train station in Venice, and when he set foot on his beloved island of Murano.

At the train station, as he stepped off the train and his feet touched Venetian soil, Uncle Ruggero began to sob. All the tension from the years in an internment camp materialized in tears that streamed from his eyes with profusion.

Outside the train station, he could only see blurry, glassy-distorted buildings through the chinks of his wet eyelids. Uncle walked down the steps, as if he had been stunned by a blow. He took one step, swayed to the right, then left. He stopped. He turned around as if in a daze. He headed towards the canal.

As the train conductor passed Uncle, he asked, "Is everything fine, *giovanotto*?"

"*Si, Si,*" Uncle said, "*si, grazie.*"

In his mind, Uncle assured himself that he was almost home. He wiped his tears and breathed a sigh of relief. Entranced, he looked at the deserted streets of Venice, engulfed in deep sleep. Venice seemed so different! Not the self-reassuring Venice that had basked in the self-importance of its history, of its ancient people, but a more timid Venice, one which was silently pondering, meditating. A Venice that asked questions but could find no answers.

No doubt his perception of Venice reflected his own feelings towards life. Uncle Ruggero had changed a great deal during the war, but Venice had remained the same. Physically untouched by the war, her beauty remained unblemished.

Silence. He could hear nothing but silence. He wished the church bells would ring to announce his arrival and to forewarn his parents, his dear beloved wife, the whole island of Murano, that he was coming home. He relaxed a little. A smile surfaced on his lips. Ruggero looked around for someone to talk to. A certain someone to tell his story to, someone to shout to, "I'm home. I have survived."

He heard the meow of a meandering cat, perhaps looking for shelter like he was. In the dark, he saw a hand waving and two eyes looking in his direction from the canal.

"Hey, you. Do you need a ride? Where are you going?" a shadow of a man in a small rowboat said.

To Murano. I'm going to see my mama. I'm going to see my wife. God, thank you, he cried from within, but he could not speak.

Uncle said he repeated those words aloud, as in a litany, a thousand times during the war while in the internment camp. Night after night, he had laid in his narrow, rickety bunk, freezing, staring into the darkness, thinking that he would go mad reciting those very words. It was a self-imposed exercise so as not to forget that life prevailed beyond the stark façade of the prisoners, and the ugly faces of the guards.

"My mama, my wife, my family, Murano. God, please protect me. Let me live. I'm too young to die..."

During the night, when his stomach had been tied up in knots from hunger and longing, he reiterated those words like he did his prayers as a child sitting next to his Mama during the Vespers at the Church of *San Pietro Martire*.

"Let him live, God. Let him come home to us," his mother, his wife Lina, and the family echoed his words.

Uncle Ruggero was great at describing events. He made everyone feel as if they had been there. He described the moment the rowboat left the train station, the gentle swishing as it moved forward, towards the open lagoon on its way to Murano, guided by the even strokes of the expert *gondoliere*.

Elio, the *gondoliere*, had stood guard for months at the train station in Venice to escort home any soldier who, like Uncle Ruggero, arrived in the heart of night. He did it as a small offering to the Virgin Mary for bringing his own son back home, safe from the war.

During the trip down the canals, through the Venetian Lagoon, Uncle Ruggero sat in the front of the rowboat coughing, sobbing. He wiped his tears with the sleeves of his jacket as Elio eyed him from the back.

The rowboat finally arrived in Murano.

"You are home, Ruggero," Elio said.

Uncle was not listening.

"You are home, Ruggero," Elio repeated. "Let me help you."

Before Elio finished his sentence, Uncle Ruggero had crawled out of the boat, and yelling, he limped toward his wife, his mama and papa, his family. . .his future.

Elio stood there waiting for any sign of life coming from within Uncle's parents' dwelling. For a switch to turn on, or for a faint light to pierce through the cracks of the green, closed shutters. He expected Uncle Ruggero's family to burst into the courtyard in their night garments, and to embrace him.

"Lina, Mama, Papa!" Uncle Ruggero shouted, looking up at the windows, cupping his mouth with one hand, while he pounded at the door with the other.

In the courtyard, a shutter slammed against the wall, and a window opened wide.

Signora Carla, the next door neighbor said to her sleepy husband, "Angelo, look, look, Ruggero has come home."

"Ruggero, Ruggero. . .Welcome home!" she shouted.

"Signora Carla!" Uncle Ruggero waved.

At that moment, his wife Lina flew down the three flights of stairs from her apartment. His mama, papa, sister Susi, Great Aunt Nice all came running towards him with open arms. They embraced and kissed him.

They embraced and kissed each other, and as they wiped tears of joy from their eyes, they entered the house and walked into the kitchen.

Uncle Ruggero suffered a lot during the war, but he came home to a loving family and to a wonderful caring community. Everyone prodded Uncle to tell his stories because they thought that every time he told them to the family, it would help him.

Uncle told us that while in the internment camp, at Erfur, he worked with the other prisoners in a stocking factory. He had many good friends among the prisoners who helped him, who prodded him to endure when his legs could barely sustain him, when his pleurisy crept in and took over his lungs. Even among the enemies, he found compassionate people who helped him through. Like the lady, head of the department at the stocking factory where he worked. She was middle aged, with a grin on her face that made the workers, at first, want to regurgitate their meager rations when she came around. The first time Uncle Ruggero saw her, she was hollering at one of the prisoners. She pushed him around, raved and ranted, just like she later did to Uncle.

The lady approached Uncle, yelling. She pushed his frail, long, bony frame into the wall. As she screamed at him, she thrust in his hand a piece of bread and a tiny cube of sugar. He was so confused that he tripped and almost fell. But as the lady helped my uncle to his feet, she looked into his eyes for a few seconds, and then left him standing there. They were expressive, compassionate eyes that pierced his heart, the eyes of a mother who found her son in every young man she met.

Uncle said that many years after the war, he received a letter from the husband of the lady supervisor at the stocking factory. The lady had recently died, and her husband had found Uncle Ruggero's address in one of her dresser drawers.

He wrote, "Dear Sir, I'm writing to you because I found your address among my wife's belongings. I just wanted to tell you that my wife has died. I wanted to write because I thought that if she kept your address in the drawer for such a long time, you must have meant something to her. Sincerely."

Now, when Uncle thought about the woman, he felt a warm feeling coming over him. He guessed she must have had a son fighting in the war, someone close to his own age.

Uncle also talked about the German guard who every day followed him into the latrines. When the guard noticed that Uncle Ruggero could not stand up, he handed him a small bag of food which Uncle shared with his two best friends. At the end of the war, when Uncle told this story to his mama and papa, filled with emotions they said, "We are going to find this man. We want to personally thank him."

After they researched the guard's whereabouts, my grandparents traveled by train to Austria to thank the man who helped their son. Thus, began a special friendship that lasted through their lifetime.

For years, my grandmother talked about how love can be found even in the most remote places.

"Sometimes," she pondered as if to herself, "love can be found even at the very bottom of a huge hole."

The family knew she meant hell. We knew she meant the war.

Funny how things work on this earth. While a German mother helped Uncle Ruggero, Grandmother, together with her lady friends, hid a few young Germans toward the end of the war. She brought them food, and gave them Uncle Ruggero's clothes.

"I hope someone does the same for my sons, Ruggero and Rino," she said.

Uncle Ruggero was different from his brother, Uncle Rino, who fought for the partisan group in the mountains. No one knew Uncle Rino's whereabouts during the war, or any of his actions. He went wherever he was needed. Uncle Rino never, ever talked about his war experiences. If he had memories, good or bad, he kept them to himself.

As a child, I once heard the adults talking about the war. They said that, in all of its evil, there was a positive facet to the war, for the war brought forth much progress in the scientific field.

"Yes," they all agreed, "war acts as a catalyst for scientific and medical progress."

I doubt that my grandmother saw the war that way. I doubt that most mothers would even think about the progress and the positive aspects a war brought forward as they waited in anguish for their sons to return home.

Mama said that my grandmother's heart ached silently, until she died, seeing her son Ruggero, a six foot three, handsome young man metamorphosed into a frail grown man. It took quite a few years for Uncle Ruggero to regain his health. Good thing that my grandparents had money to pay for the best and most advanced medical care for him.

Mama also pointed out that after the war, Grandmother wrote to every bureaucratic War Office in Italy to petition for Uncle Ruggero to receive a war pension. Year after year, she wrote to government officials, undeterred by all the rejections, determined to ensure that her son received what he deserved for his valorous contribution to the war.

The letter from the War Office telling her that, yes, he was eligible to receive the Veteran's Pension arrived the day after Grandmother died.

Mama said it was too bad that Grandmother had died a day too early, or one could say that the much anticipated letter arrived a day too late, for her to rejoice.

After Mama read the letter, she said to us in her quiet composure, "*Nonna* has accomplished her mission. Now, she can rest in peace."

Papa and the TV

When TV became an integral part of the household furniture in Murano, Papa adamantly refused to buy one. As he sat in his chair at the head of the table, before, during, and after dinner, he prognosticated with conviction on the effect TV would have on our society.

"TV is going to break the family unit. Instead of talking to each other, people are going to stare at that small square." As he said that, he formed a rectangular shape with his fingers and stuck his nose through it.

"How do you like that? No, No. TV will never enter my house," Papa said. "I want us to visit, to talk, to have fun together."

When Mama said, "Bambini, you know we do not have the money to buy a TV," we told her that we could go without fruit for a while, or that we could eat a small plastic cup of Nutella, creamy chocolate spread, as a main course like some of our friends had done to save money to buy their TVs. As we said that, we knew how absurd it was to suggest that we forgo the fruit or the main dish in order to save for something Papa did not approve of. It was rather preposterous to even insinuate that we cut down on food because no angel from heaven could have swayed Papa into giving up a complete meal. It did no good to beg, to make Papa laugh, to entertain him after dinner with dancing, with the Sound of Music-type songs as Papa stuck to his convictions, until. . .Uncle Paolo gave us his old black and white TV and Papa did not have the courage to refuse it.

Papa put the new/old TV in the living room out of everyone's sight. The TV only worked if you pounded on all sides of the wooden case. Even when the picture came on, horizontal lines invaded the screen, and we could only hear voices and see irregular black and white lines.

Of course, we children were excited about the TV. When I told Tina that Papa had relented and we had a TV, even though TV was not a novelty for Tina, she did not waste any time to say, "Let's go to your house and watch it."

I led the way.

When we entered the living room, Piero and Tina's brother were pounding on each side and on the back of our "new" TV as if trying to prevent it from choking. Clowning around, they made all kind of prognoses about its malady.

"This TV has bronchitis," Piero said, stepping back, scratching his chin.

"No, she has ammonia."

"You mean pneumonia, don't you, Dr. Tulio?"

"Actually, I think she has a case of amnesia. Her mind is fuzzy, blurred by jagged lines. Her behavior is indiscernible."

"Dr. Tulio," summed up my brother, "I think she has a strong case of old age. Why don't we just give her a last jolt and then let it be?"

Margherita and Tina's sister, Elisa, were there as well. They sat on two chairs as in a theater in front of the lined screen laughing at Piero and Tulio's dialogue, laughing at the new TV. For an instant, I was embarrassed, but Tina was too good a friend and too pragmatic to dwell on something like a broken TV, and within seconds from our entrance, we joined Elisa and Margherita, laughing ourselves silly. From then on the TV rested comatose in the corner of the living room.

We did not miss the TV because Papa continued to tell us stories, but I missed joining in my friends' conversations when they talked about the various TV programs.

Enchanting Tales

"Papa, Mama, tell us the stories of when we were born," we implored. There were no misgivings of how we came into this world because our parents chiseled the facts in our small, pretty heads with such mystery and enthusiasm that the stories became our "facts of life."

Papa found Gabri all bundled up in a pink blanket inside a wicker basket on the church steps. The stork left Antonio on a foggy November morning outside the white, marble windowsill of Mama and Papa's bedroom. I was born in the field adjacent to our house under a cauliflower leaf. Margherita's rosy cheeks and smiling face surfaced from a patch of white daisies in Great Aunt Nice and Aunt Susi's back yard. Papa brought home Piero, and as he entrusted the baby on Gabri's lap, he said, "This is your little brother. I found him on a boat in *Fondamenta Dei Vetrai*. When I went by, I heard him calling, 'Papa!'" The mailman delivered Giuliana inside a lovely pink, square box tied with a gold and pink ribbon. We were not so sure about Gelmina because she always joked that she was born in a chicken coop, amongst all the chicken shit.

Mama and Papa made no qualms about painting their colorful versions of the miracle of life because that is what people did in the late 1950's and early 60's, and of course during our grandparents' generation as well.

In agreement that children did not need to know "things" too early in life, they relied on their imaginations to fulfill our curiosity. As far as I could remember, when Mama's stomach became large, the butcher said, as he came around the counter and careened to caress our cheeks with his index and middle fingers in an up and down movement, almost shouting to make us understand more clearly what he was saying, "Your Mama is getting big. She has eaten the moon. Watch the moon, tonight, you'll see how small the moon has become."

Quite pleased with himself he would add, "Tell your mama to eat steaks instead of eating the moon. We need the moon to light the sky."

"My Mama did not eat the moon," Gabri, daring for her age, replied, hand on her hip, tapping the tip of her shoe on the marble floor, looking up at the butcher.

"She didn't?" Surprised, the butcher said, "And what did she eat?"

"She ate a watermelon."

"Oh, a watermelon. And who told you that?" he asked, laughing.

"Sister Clementina," Gabri answered, all proud to let the butcher know that she knew all about Mama's big belly. While Mama placed her hand on Gabri's head to motion her to be respectful, and not to answer or defy adults, Antonio and I hung on to Mama's skirt, asked no questions and gave no replies. We kept quiet for Mama always said that her Mama had told her, "Children should be seen but not heard." So we just listened, satisfied with Gabri's interjection, pleased to know that our Mama did not eat the moon, but rather a watermelon.

We children enjoyed listening to Mama and Papa's birth stories more than the one Sele's mother told her because her mother's stories made Sele cry.

Sele's mother, a pretty brunette, meticulous in her coiffure, with short wisps framing her oval face, and big, white upper- teeth smiling all over the streets of Murano, always wore the latest fashions. As she walked, swaying her hips, she looked at her reflection in the shops' windows pretending to fix her perfect hair glued together with a beer lacquer. The way she dressed, walked and talked she did not look like a mama at all.

One day, outside our grammar school, I overheard Sele's mother, a "modern thinker," tell Mama that she was going to explain to Sele the facts of life because she thought her Sele was mature enough to understand the truth.

Mama, who did not agree with her, replied that she preferred we remained innocent a little while longer.

When Sele's mother told Sele the facts of life, it turned out that Sele was not as mature as her mother thought her to be. At age seven, Sele came to school with puffy red eyes, and when I asked her what was the matter, amidst many tears she told me, "My mama told me how babies are born. I do not want to have babies that way."

I did not ask her any questions as I knew how babies came about. My siblings and I were experts on the subject. When our friends gathered around Sele and asked me, "Why is she crying?" I announced, "She is crying because her stomach hurts."

Turning to Sele I whispered in her ear, "Come to my house on Sunday after lunch, and my Mama is going to tell you some stories."

On Sunday, Sele came to our house.

I asked, "Mama, tell us where you found me."

Eager to please, Papa and Mama looked at each other and began.

"Early one winter morning, I heard a faint cry," Mama said. "I wondered where the cry was coming from, and if I should get up. Snug in bed, next to your papa, I looked at him all bundled up wearing his white woolen hat, snoring, dreaming, smiling like a baby. As the minutes went by, the cry became a scream, 'OHAAAA, OHAAAAA, OHAAAA.'"

I beamed at Sele who looked at me with pleasure, happy that I had screamed loud enough for Mama to hear me.

Cognizant that perhaps something special was about to happen to her family, Mama woke up Papa, and without a word, they both jumped out of bed. They listened for a moment to make sure the crying was still coming from the nearby field. Then they ran to the door, grabbed and threw their coats over their shoulders, hurried in their bare feet down the stairs, and on to the icy dirt amidst the frosted cauliflower leaves.

"The crying had stopped," Mama said. "We kept on looking under every leaf, up and down the unkempt rows of frozen cauliflowers, until, behind the peach tree, under a purple leaf with a speck of ice on her little nose, a beautiful baby girl smiled up at us."

"Your mama cried," Papa said. "We were so happy to see your small little face. Yes, I knew you were our special little girl. The third child, like me."

"Beautiful?" Gelmina uttered with a smirk on her face. "You were so ugly, Anna."

Addressing us children, she added, "Look at your mother. You cannot say that you were ugly because she starts crying. Anna, when you were born, you looked like a piece of coal, with long, thick black hair and purple skin."

"She was not ugly, Gelmina. You should not say those things," Papa admonished.

"Mama, did you go to the field in your nightgown?" Pietro said.

Before Mama could answer, Gelmina said, to make us laugh, "Can you imagine your father in his white nightgown, with his bare, skinny legs running outside?"

I turned to look at Sele seated next to me and placed my hand on hers. I knew Sele was having fun.

"Tell us about the boat. Pietro. . .how he called you, Papa," Margherita said.

"No, I want Margherita's story," I said.

On Mama's birthday, Papa went to Great Aunt Nice and Aunt Susi's house to get flowers because if you had no money to buy flowers from the florist, you went into their garden and picked fresh flowers there.

"When I got to their house," Papa said, "Great Aunt Nice and Aunt Susi were all excited."

"Nico," they said, "there is a surprise for you and Teresa in our garden. Go and see, but be careful where you step."

Papa paused, then said, "Teresa, remember how happy we were when I found Margherita?"

With garden clippers in his hand, Papa went on his own into the garden while Great Aunt Nice and Aunt Susi waited in their kitchen. He walked on the dirt path that led to the small piece of land in the back of the house. He passed the colorful zinnias, and the pomegranate and two fig trees. He glanced around, looking for Mama's favorite flower, the daisies, which he found in the corner growing with profusion, swaying in the gentle breeze. Smiling at the sunshine, the daisies murmured to him, "*Vieni, Vieni più vicino*, Papa. Come, come closer, Papa."

Stooping towards the earth, Papa snipped at the daisies, carefully cutting in a circular motion around the perimeter. He pondered on the miracle of nature as he placed each one in a round bouquet. He began to sing one of his favorite opera pieces, *"Oh fanciulla all'imbruni-i-ir, dimmi vuoi da me veni-I-ir... non dir di no. . ."*

He stopped.

Startled, he thought he heard a giggle. He turned his head to see if Great Aunt Nice and Aunt Susi had followed him, but no one was there. He looked at the tall, red brick wall that divided the yard from the elementary school, thinking that perhaps a child was trying to climb over the wall. No head appeared there. He looked up at Uncle Ruggero's apartment windows to see if Aunt Lina was hanging her laundry, but the green shutters were closed.

He stopped to listen again.

Out of the corner of his eye, he saw something moving among the patch of daisies. He bent down, and with the palms of his hands, he pushed the daisies aside. There, with a smiling face and rosy cheeks, lay a laughing baby.

"I bent down closer and saw Margherita's eyes taking in the universe, digesting it with pleasure. Her little mouth was shaped like a heart. She looked so delicate: just like the face of an angel in a Fra Filippo Lippi painting. When she saw me, Margherita kicked her feet up in the air and waved her tight fist at me. I picked her up and whispered in her ear, "Margherita, Margherita, my little Margherita."

Proud and excited, holding his Margherita up high in front of him like a delicate piece of pastry, Papa walked into Great Aunt Nice and Aunt Susi's kitchen who were waiting, ready to follow him home. With Papa in the front, Great Aunt Nice and Aunt Susi trailed behind towards the bridge of *San Pietro Martire*.

"Nico, another little girl. Stop, let me see her," Lena, Mama's friend who was watering the geraniums shouted from her second-story apartment window.

Lena ran down the two flights of stairs. Amidst ahhhs and ooohs, she, as well, trailed towards Mama's house in the procession, still wearing her apron, slippers, and her rollers. She spoke to the passersby, to the owners of the fruit store and the tobacco store. Smiling to everyone, Papa went by each shop holding Margherita like an oracle. People stopped what they were doing, came out on the street and complimented him on his little Margherita.

With our eyes focused on Papa, we all listened to his stories. When he finished telling us about Margherita, Antonio and Pietro began pounding on the table, wanting Gelmina to tell her very own story.

"Gel-mi-na, Gel-mi-na, Gel-mi-na."

"Me?" Gelmina said blushing. "There is nothing to talk about. My parents. . .poor parents. Did not even notice when I was born. Nine children. We raised ourselves. . .really."

As she paused to reflect, Gelmina added, "When I was little, I spent all my time in the chicken coop. If I was hungry, I ate raw eggs. I do not want to remember."

"Tell us," we insisted, "about when you went with your sister at four in the morning in the cold of winter, with no socks or coat, to pump water from the fountain in the main square."

Lowering her voice, as if talking to herself, Gelmina said, "Yes, we suffered cold and hunger. Every third morning, since I was five, my father sent me and my four-year-old sister to the town square three miles from our house. With a donkey, one wine barrel on each side of it, we walked holding hands in the cold, dark morning, together with children from nearby farms. We went to pump water from the community fountain. *Che vita*! It's better to forget."

Gelmina grew up on a farm, a one-hour boat ride from Murano. She ran away from home at sixteen because she did not want to work in the fields. That is when she landed at our house. Mama said that a few weeks after Gelmina arrived, Papa took her back to her family to make peace with them because he could not conceive of a young girl not talking to her parents. Gelmina agreed to go, but only if Papa stayed around during her visit.

Gelmina's life was marred by many secrets. The cold wind from the north howled of German soldiers eating and drinking at Gelmina's family farm. It whispered of terrified children, and a frightened mother. The wind murmured of two young girls hiding behind the fruit trees, or running through the field to the neighboring farm. What the wind did not relay, we discerned from a sentence, a phrase, a word scattered here and there. We learned to catch words thrown in the air at random. Like the wine Gelmina's family fermented each fall, after churning those words in our mind for a few days, a new story came through, complete.

Wanting to end the conversation, Gelmina tried to steer it in Sele's direction. She got up from her chair, walked towards the sink and said, "*Sele bella*, did you like our stories? Are you going to the movies this afternoon? Hurry if you want to catch the cowboy movies because the priest is not going to wait for you."

Excited to have shared our stories with Sele, we went to see the two cowboy movies at the church theater. Towards the end of the movies, when the U.S. Cavalry arrived on the scene, we all stood up on the wooden seats, jumped up and down, clapped our hands, and shouted at the top of our voices, "Cowboys,Indians. Cowboys,Indians. Cowboys, Indians."

Cowboys and Indians, Margherita and Gelmina's stories, my Uncles' stories, the neighbor's stories. . .we did not need the TV to entertain us.

In particular, we loved when Mama told us her favorite story about her Grandfather Giuseppe Barovier. I knew she enjoyed talking about him because her pride radiated from her eyes and fell on us like the projection of a lighthouse on a boat at sea. One could tell from the smile in her eyes how proud she was of him and of his achievements, of his enthusiasm and of his innovative spirit in the art of glass making. Mama was proud of her Grandfather Giuseppe for having the courage to realize his dream. She treasured with pride her grandfather's classic pieces that she kept in an antique curio in the entrance hall of our apartment. It was a portion of his collection of hundreds of miniature prototypes of the original ones, which he left as part of his estate to be divided among all of his heirs.

When we begged Mama to talk about her Grandfather, she complied with pleasure. Arms folded on her lap, slouching a little, legs crossed under the table, she laced an enchanting tale, carefully stitching it together with the same dexterity and care as when she embroidered our dowries. She meant her tale to be handed down for many generations to come; one which, for sure, would make us, our own children, and grandchildren proud.

Great Grandfather Giuseppe

With our eyes on Mama, we all listened. Mama told us that her Grandfather Giuseppe Barovier, born in 1853, won, at age seventeen, in Queen Victoria's London, the gold cross of the Court of St. Giacomo. He received as well many personal accolades at the world International Exposition of Vienna, Graz, Milan and many others.

From an early age, Giuseppe turned every scrap of paper he found into a work of art. He scribbled chicken scratches on top of newspaper articles even before his father read them. He pounded square nails into pieces of wood he found by the kitchen stove, piled them up on top of each other and constructed tall, geometric abstract objects. He moved the furniture and created circles, squares, and every form and shape he could think of, and always called his mama to come and admire his creations.

"Bravo, Giuseppe," his Mama said over the constant confusion of their kitchen. She encouraged all her thirteen children, as they crawled, ran, marched and climbed in all corners of the two-story house in which they lived.

She talked and addressed her husband in the third-person as it was the custom at that particular time, as if her husband and the owner of the glass factory were two different people. She ordered her husband, "Signor Barovier, tomorrow, bring home from the glass factory cardboard and paper for Giuseppe to draw on. He is the artist in the family."

At ten years of age, Giuseppe drew small delicate objects shaped like the ones he had seen at the Museum in Murano, and the one he put together in his mind from the pieces of glass he found in the empty field by the church. He sketched cups, bottles, glasses of different shapes and styles. He drew fountains, piece by piece, and elaborate constructions with the quill his father used to write letters. At times, he scribbled on the sidewalk and on the bridge steps. When his Mama was not looking, he transferred his creativity to the side façade of their house with a piece of coal he took from the chicken coop.

At the end of the school year, his proud mother announced during dinner, as she held up a large, rectangular gold paper with a black inscription on it, "Look, this is Giuseppe's fifth grade diploma."

The whole family clapped. They laughed and clapped. They patted Giuseppe's shoulders and slapped his head. Angela, the only sister, got up, made a pirouette and danced around the table until her mama told her to sit down and pay attention.

"Tomorrow," Giuseppe's mama said pointing her index finger to the ceiling, "Signor Sergio is going to take Giuseppe to the glass factory."

Giuseppe smiled and lowered his head. He wanted to go to work in his papa's factory. He wanted to create, to pull, to shape, to rotate and blow into the long narrow pipe. He wished to circle the metal implement around the fire-ball of molten glass like he had seen his papa do. He wanted to become a *Master Vetraio* like his papa and his grandfather, and sign his creations like Master Vittorio who had worked in his papa's factory for twenty years.

Like a magician, Giuseppe dreamed of mixing different colors together and of creating new ones as he did in school with his best friend Andrea.

The next morning, Giuseppe got up at four-thirty with his mama and papa. He rinsed his face, combed his short curly hair, and put on a brand new wool undershirt his mama had laid on the chair by the stove for him, to protect his skin from the heat of the hot furnace. He dipped the day-old toasted bread in his milk and coffee, and finished his breakfast in haste because his papa was waiting for him at the door.

Giuseppe felt proud. Today he was a man, like his papa.

He walked by his papa's side holding his hand in the dark deserted *fondamenta*, lit only by the moonlight. The soft tapping of their heels reverberated on the cobblestones. As his eye acclimated to the dark, Giuseppe noticed that the water in the canal was cobalt blue. The same shade as the plate 25" in diameter his papa had designed and manufactured for the Bishop of Venice when he honored them with his visit at the glass factory.

As Giuseppe and his papa walked, Giuseppe noticed the half moon and stars up in the sky, and stared enthralled at the moon's reflection on the canal. The moon, rocking back and forth in the creased water, Giuseppe's head moving up and down, observing first the still, watchful moon in the sky, and then at the playful one in the water. He wished to touch the reflection of the moon to see if there was magic in it.

Giuseppe thought of taking the moon with his small hand, and placing it on the clear glass vase he imagined making. He was puzzled at the moon, which had burst out of the sky and into the water, but which could still be seen up in the sky. He felt his heart racing out of his body from the excitement and looked for it in the canal's water.

Father and son walked hand in hand through *Fondamenta Dei Vetrai*. They crossed the *Santa Chiara* Bridge. At the fifth gong of the clock tower, they stepped over the threshold of the brown, double door of the glass factory's entrance.

"Papa, what am I going to do today? Can I hold the steel pipe for you?" Giuseppe said.

"Today, just watch. Watch and learn," his papa said.

Once inside the large rectangular room with white painted walls, which he had only seen a few times before, Giuseppe stood for a moment in the center of the room, mouth agape. His ears stood up like a rabbit. His eyes wide, he observed everything, as he was eager to learn about the art of glass making. Like the earth, he slowly rotated on his axis, arms dangling at his side, one hand holding a small leaf of paper and a pencil. Three huge, dome-shaped enclosures lined with refractory bricks occupied the center of the furnace room. All around the brick wall, Giuseppe noticed several rectangular openings with a fiery *inferno* on the inside where he knew the *Maestro* would insert a steel pipe with glass on the end to mold it into a paste and then turn it into a refined object.

Giuseppe was proud to be in the furnace room. He was proud to learn all about the molten glass because his papa had said that the art of glass making was the "bread and butter" of all of the families in Murano. Yes, he remembered when his papa said those words, "bread and butter." Giuseppe understood what his papa meant because when his papa said it, his eyes sparkled like the glimmers of gold in the chandelier that hung from the ceiling of their dining room. Giuseppe never forgot his father's words.

"Giuseppe," he said, "for the *Muranesi* the art of glass-making is as precious as the discovery of gold in California. Like the gold, we extract the primary ingredients from the soil of the surrounding areas, the Mediterranean coast. If we use the creativity that God has given us and our ingenuity we can survive. We can be successful."

When his father said that, Giuseppe nodded his head in acknowledgment, and then ran out in the courtyard and capered among the flowers, leaping from one rock to the next.

On a different occasion, his papa had explained to him that the Muranesi glass blowers used the same type of glass the medieval glass workers had used. The primary ingredients, very fine sand and soda, were extracted from the ashes of plants from the Mediterranean coast. When inserted in the hot furnace at a specific temperature, the mixture melted so that it could be shaped into different objects.

Now, in the room where his papa and Signor Vittorio worked, Giuseppe's heart was on fire, too. The heat within molded his thoughts into a chaotic state. He stood in awe and was engulfed by every little detail of the room's layout.

All around the furnaces, at each station, a wooden working bench, a stool with a bucket full of water and several different implements rested on the bench, or hung on square nails. At each station, a maestro with two subordinate workers, the *servente* and the *serventino* were ready to start.

"Sit there, Giuseppe," he heard his papa's say as he felt a hand pushing him towards a bench adjacent to one of the furnaces. Giuseppe sat without saying a word. He glanced and nodded his head to the other two boys, who like him, had graduated from fifth grade and were starting their working career that same day.

"Come on, let's move. Gianni, grab the blow pipe, let's go, let's go-o-o," *Maestro* Vittorio shouted in an authoritative voice.

Gianni grabbed a black, huge glove and put it on his right hand to protect it from the heat. He inserted the blow-pipe into the furnace. He gathered and wrapped around it some of the molten glass from the shovel inside the furnace, and turned his head to see if the boys on the bench were watching him perform.

"Gianni, hold that pipe higher, for Christ's sake, and rotate it to balance the glass. How many times do I have to tell you that?"

Gianni kept his mouth closed, but the maestro's impatient voice told Giuseppe that accuracy was a must in the art of glass making and that Gianni, who was *primo servente,* should have known better.

Maestro Vittorio blew into the pipe several times to form a bubble. He handed the blow pipe back and forth to Gianni to insert it into the hot furnace to prevent the glass from cooling off.

With each blow, Giuseppe saw a new object come alive and played a guessing game in his mind.

They are making a glass bowl. No, they are making part of a chandelier, or perhaps the base of a fountain, Giuseppe thought with enthusiasm.

He liked fountains. In particular, the one with three levels where the water flowed smooth and transparent from one level to the next, reflecting throughout a myriad of multicolored specks, the colors of the rainbow. He dreamed of designing and making a three-level fountain with small flowers all around the edges, and on its base. Someday he was going to design his own fountain and call it the *Millefiori Fontana.* He liked that name, the Fountain of a Thousand Flowers. He was eager to begin a small glass-fountain, a prototype for his glass collection like his papa made every time he designed a new glass object, and a real one for his front yard for everyone to admire.

Giuseppe heard the maestro shouting orders at the *serventino,* a boy a little older than Giuseppe, who like a kangaroo, hopped here, there and everywhere. The boy ran back and forth handing the various tools to the *servente* and the *maestro,* returning the implements to their proper places after their use, filling the bucket with water, running errands, and making sure that he performed each task in the order they were given.

Through the two doors that led to the outside courtyard, people came in and out to ask questions, to deliver different products, to check that everyone was at their stations, that commissions were in the making, and that things were in order and running as they should.

While the maestro rotated the pipe several times, first to the right, then left to balance the molten glass, and to center it, he flattened the base with a special hinged tool. And with each step, each blow, the bubble grew into a larger dimension.

Angelo, the boy seated next to Giuseppe, said, "*Ti ga visto Giuseppe come che el maestro sofia dentro dela cana?*" "Giuseppe, did you see how the *Maestro* blows into the pipe?"

"It's easy. My father said I can learn if I pay attention," said Toni, the one seated at the end of the bench.

"What are you saying?" Giuseppe interjected. "Are you crazy? My papa told me that it takes years to learn to blow, mold and shape an art object." Giuseppe was annoyed at his friend's nonchalance. For sure he was better informed than his two friends.

"Easy," he said. There was nothing easy about the art of glassmaking. Giuseppe knew that it would not be easy to excel, to become a *maestro*, to distinguish himself among the best, to someday have his name engraved at the Museum in Murano, and to have writers write books about his skills as a glass blower and as a designer. Yes, that was Giuseppe's dream.

His papa always said that dreams are the source, the birth of great things, and that without dreams man would have a ghastly emptiness inside. Giuseppe knew that if he wanted to tread in his father's footsteps, he would have to work hard and in earnest. Someday, he would achieve his dream.

At the end of the story Mama would say with pride, "Yes, my grandfather, Giuseppe Barovier, was a skillful craftsman, and a gifted designer."

The Encyclopedia Lady

One day, Papa came home for lunch, sat at the table, stared out of the window at the gray sky, at the few birds flying about, and sighed. I could see that he was sad.

Mama said, "He is thinking about his friend Pieretto. He is feeling his pains." Pieretto's wife, the foreigner from Venice, had died, and Papa had just come back from her funeral. Mama did not say what kind of sickness she suffered. She only said that the foreigner suffered a lot the last few days of her life. She mouthed the name of her sickness to Gelmina who slowly moved her head back and forth, and said, "Peace to her soul."

"I think your Papa is afraid of death," Mama said.

I had never heard Papa say that he was afraid of dying. I only heard him joke, "Hung by a nail, but on this earth."

I did not believe Papa was afraid to die because we all knew that he was going to heaven.

I stared at Papa in silence during lunch. I looked in his eyes for a sign, for a trace on his face, for an inkling which could tell me he was afraid.

I followed the corrugated lines on his forehead, the ones on his small mouth, but only read in them a deep sadness.

After lunch, Papa got up and walked to the kitchen window. I followed him and leaned against his side. He put his arm around my shoulder, and we stared in silence at the people going by. Then, Papa kissed me and went back to work. I remained there a few more minutes to watch him disappear behind the tall brick building.

The cold, gusty north wind slammed repeatedly against our apartment building and at our windows. From our warm kitchen, I observed the dark gray sky, the swirling dust, and thought perhaps snowflakes would soon fall from the sky. I watched passersby bundled in thick winter coats, scarves, and leather gloves as they hurried home to warm themselves by a stove. I helped Mama by putting a few coal pieces in the wood stove since Mama was busy sewing a coat for Margherita, and Gelmina was washing the dishes.

"It must be several degrees below zero outside. Cover yourself well when you go out," Mama said.

I did not want to go to my math lesson at Signora Maria's, but Mama never let us stay home. I knocked several times at the bathroom door. Pietro was inside.

I walked into my bedroom to pick up my notebook, but Margherita, who was studying, yelled at me, "Get out of here. I have a test tomorrow. Mamaaa."

I entered the *salotto*, where Gabri sat on the couch reading a novel, wrapped in a woolen blanket. She looked at me as if to ask why had I entered. I said nothing and went back to the kitchen. I heard the bathroom door open and raced in before anyone else got there. I locked the door, and shivered.

It was so cold, icy cold.

Mama always said we were lucky that our kitchen was nice and warm. We were luckier than Signora Olga, the neighbor upstairs, or Signora Alice, the neighbor downstairs. Both families had been trying to save money to pay for their house mortgage, and this was the second winter they did not have heat in their houses. When we heard a tap on the door, we knew it was Signora Alice.

"How is everybody?" Signora Alice said as she hopped in Mama's kitchen, coffee pot in her hand. "I came to warm myself and drink a cup of coffee." She sat down across from Mama so that they could chat.

While in the bathroom, I heard the doorbell and heard Mama's voice asking, "Who is it?"

I did not recognize the voice of the person who entered. I went into the kitchen to say goodbye to Mama and to Gelmina, and there sat a middle-aged woman on the edge of a chair, both of her arms resting on the kitchen table. She was explaining to Mama, who continued to sew, why she should buy us children *The Encyclopedia for Young Adults*.

As the woman talked, Mama nodded her head in assent.

"It's nice to be inside," the woman said. She was still wearing her coat, all faded and worn. Her face was ashen from the freezing cold, and her frozen, swollen hands couldn't turn the thick pages of her book.

She paused for a few seconds, then said, "You have a bright fire on the stove. Do you use coal or wood? Does the stove warm up the whole house?" She did not notice that the kitchen door was closed. She had not yet asked to go to the bathroom and did not know that the other rooms in the house had a temperature of below zero.

I saw Mama and Gelmina look at each other. Gelmina asked the lady if she wanted an espresso coffee. The woman's eyes brightened.

"Thank you," she said. "I would like to have a cup of coffee very much. I have been walking all morning in the cold weather."

She fell silent, perhaps trying to decide whether to share her information.

"I came from the country. I was hoping to sell at least one encyclopedia today. They are wonderful books, you know."

She gave Mama her sales pitch, words she had repeated a thousand times before.

I stared at the Encyclopedia lady's face, and now, after she had been in the kitchen for a few minutes, her pale skin took on a rosy luster. Her fine hair touched her shoulders, and her fringed bangs fell over her high forehead. She talked, talked, and talked, and at five-thirty, when I returned home from Signora Maria's house, she was still there, talking.

The Encyclopedia woman was now peeling potatoes by the kitchen sink, talking to Gelmina. As my siblings and I came into the kitchen, Mama pointed to the lady and explained to each of us and to our friends, "This lady is selling encyclopedias."

At the mention of the word encyclopedia, the woman turned around and smiled but did not attempt to sell anything. Everyone nodded, not knowing whether to ask questions or to keep on doing what they were doing.

I moseyed towards Mama and whispered, "Is she staying for dinner?"

"I do not have anything good to eat," Mama mouthed. "Well, maybe I can add some *frittatine* to the chicken broth. I think she is hungry."

I nodded and then joined Margherita and Elisa who were playing Monopoly at the kitchen table. Now the woman was cleaning the string beans.

The kitchen, enveloped in the delicate aromatic smell of food, was full of people. Warm vapor sneaked out of the covered pan Mama used for the broth, and the smell of fried *frittatine*, eggs scrambled with flour, milk and herbs, permeated throughout. Mama strained the broth to separate it from the one chicken that was going to feed eleven people. She was good at placing the food on the serving dishes so that it looked like more than enough for at least one round.

Mama made sure she got every little piece of meat off the chicken bones and placed it in the center of a huge oval white dish, seasoning it with salt, pepper and olive oil. She molded *Insalata Russa* all around the chicken, a mixture of boiled potatoes, cooked minced carrots, peas, chopped capers and tuna. She covered the mounded oval ring with a light layer of homemade mayonnaise and garnished it in a mosaic design with carrots, lemon slices, and chopped parsley as if she were one of the artists at the glass factories.

"Clear the table and start setting it," Mama said to us children. "Papa is coming home soon."

Seven-thirty on the dot, Papa entered our apartment. He took small steps as he said in a jovial tone, "*Che bel caldo.* Teresa, are we ready?"

He walked towards the stove, lifted the pan's covers and said, "And what do we have for dinner tonight? Oh, yes, *frittatine in brodo.* Teresa, *bambini,* come to the table."

"I see we are having guests tonight," Papa said when he noticed the woman. He moved towards her and extended his hand.

"*Piacere* Nico," he introduced himself. He did not ask who she was, or why she was there.

"Elisa, are you eating with us, too?" he said. "Gelmina, add an extra plate for Elisa."

Elisa tried to explain that she needed to go home, but Papa insisted. "You have a wonderful mother. Oh yes, I know your grandmother well because she is second cousin to my father. They used to play together. Stay Elisa. We'd like to have you with us tonight."

We all sat, our family, the woman, and Elisa, who said to Margherita, "Your papa is so much fun."

Papa was fun. After we ate our meal, he metamorphosed into a magician. He got up, put on his white cotton gloves, and brought to the table a few objects for his magic tricks. He made a crystal glass disappear. He extracted a coin from Giuliana's nose. He took a glass of wine and emptied it into a paper bag only to make the wine reappear again in the glass a few seconds later. As he performed his tricks, he told us stories. When he was a young man, he entertained, together with his friends, all of the inhabitants of Murano during the *Festa Campestre* in the church parish—a celebration given every year to collect money to restore the interior of *San Pietro Martire* Church. He told of how much the spectators applauded his magic tricks. He talked of how hard they booed and laughed at him when his glass fell on the ground instead of disappearing on his lap.

"What wonderful memories I have. *Bambini*, we need to have good memories in our lives," Papa said.

He paused.

"Life is so short, so short, so short," he added as if to himself.

We knew he was thinking about Pieretto's wife.

At eleven-thirty, when the last guest walked down the stairs, Mama said, "*Bambini, presto, presto,* turn off the light so that no one will ring the doorbell and come for a visit."

The Encyclopedia lady returned to our house several different times. And yes, eventually, Mama did buy *The Encyclopedia for Young Adults*.

The Church and Communism

Every Sunday during lunch, throughout my adolescent years, poor Father Michele's sermon was the center of our conversation. Gabri, who sat in church next to Sister Clementina so that the two of them could sing like canaries, was very vocal about it. Margherita and I could never tell Papa what the Father had talked about because Tina, Elisa, Margherita and I bulwarked ourselves behind the main pillars of the church. That way Sister Agata would not see us talking and laughing.

Like everyone else on the island, when I talked about Father Michele, I learned to place the "poor" in front of his name. When people pronounced the adjective "poor," they elongated the o-o-o as their voices dropped a few pitches. "Poor" Father Michele this, and "poor" Father Michele that, expressed in the same sentiment one used when talking about a battered dog, or an innocent child who gets in trouble because he doesn't know any better.

Every Sunday, Poor Father Michele, with his short and stout demeanor, fat neck bulging out of his white collar, walked up to the pulpit. He placed a loose piece of scribbled lined paper on the lectern, took off his four-pointed, stiff black hat, set it on the floor, and bowed his head toward the parishioners. Before he began talking, he stepped onto a wooden stool so that his hands, which he laid limply on the carved edge of the dark, mahogany pulpit, reached the same level as his armpits.

Poor Father Michele looked pained when he delivered his holy message—speaking through his nasal passages—in a monotone that put everyone to sleep. Even with a temperature of below zero inside the church, Poor Father Michele stopped several times during the sermon to wipe the sweat off his face and to blow his nose with that same handkerchief. It was of no use to expect a meaningful sermon to reflect on throughout the week, as Poor Father Michele could not relate to people. He pretended he did not notice how fidgety they all became after just a few minutes into his speech.

In his customary ritual that lasted until his retirement, Poor Father Michele started his sermon with, *"Carissimi fratelli e sorelle* we are gathered here today to celebrate the words of Jesus Christ, *il nostro Santissimo, Reverissimo, Redentore del mondo."*

As he stretched his neck, tilting his chin up high, he looked up to the Cathedral's ceiling as if in search of inspiration from the *"Santissimo, Reverissimo, Redentore."*

During mass on Sunday morning, the children would mouth his same words, sometimes pinching their noses with their index finger and thumb to mimic his nasal intonation.

When we complained to Papa that Poor Father Michele's sermon put us all to sleep, Papa gave us his Moses version of a reply and said, "God knows best. Look at how God picked Moses to deliver his people, even though he stuttered."

However, when he wanted to sympathize with us, with a devilish smile, which made Mama's cheeks flare up, he said, "What do you expect from a priest who was voted in by the Communist Party."

As if to redeem himself in Mama's eyes, he summed up the two contrasting remarks with, "Poor Father Michele, there is no life in him."

I agreed with Papa. It looked to me as if Poor Father Michele and his old aunt who lived with him, did not have as much energy as Mama and Gelmina.

Every year, come spring, Mama and Gelmina painted the inside walls of our apartment because between the humidity and the smoke from the wood stove in the kitchen, the walls became somewhat black during the winter months. Each spring, before Poor Father Michele went door to door to bless the houses, Mama and Gelmina painted our apartment and cleaned every corner of it.

On their hands and knees, they scrubbed and shined the floor. They polished the chrome handles of the doors and windows. They dismantled and dusted each piece of the Murano-glass chandeliers that hung in each room, as well as all of the glass pieces from Mama's grandfather's collection. Windows open, they let the fresh spring air and the sunshine in, hoping the smell of fresh paint and wax escaped outside.

"In our house you can eat off the floor," Gelmina said with great satisfaction when they finished.

"At least we know why we are exhausted at the end of the day." Mama sighed.

Mama had a tremendous amount of energy and could also fix all of the electrical appliances. She took care of the house maintenance since Papa worked long hours.

"You do not expect Papa to come home after working ten hours and start painting the house or fixing things, do you?" Mama said when we asked her why Papa couldn't do those jobs.

Gelmina thought that Poor Father Michele and his aunt should have pulled their sleeves up as well and grabbed a bucket and paint brush, exercised their muscles and cleaned. Poor Father Michele lived in a two-story house owned by the church with no central heating. Every *Muranese* knew that in his house, the rooms' internal walls were black from mildew and smoke from the wood stove.

Rumors went around that during the rainy season, Poor Father Michele's aunt placed pots and pans on the floor in the upstairs bedrooms when rivulets of water dribbled through the crevices of the hundred-year-old, terracotta roof tiles.

That would never have happened in Mama's house. She would have climbed on the roof herself before anyone in Murano said something so disgraceful as that she placed pots and pans on the floor when it rained. In our house, Mama was too proud to use pots and pans for anything other than to cook a meal.

Gelmina and Mama labored a good day's work instead. With handkerchiefs tied around their hair, sleeves above their elbows, old rags on their legs to protect their slippers from possible splashes of paint, the two of them completed their spring cleaning and painting in no time.

When Mama's friends announced, "Teresa, he started his rounds yesterday," or when a lady at the bread shop or on the street stopped Gelmina and said, "Gelmina, tell Teresa that Poor Father Michele has already gone to Gigia's house, and probably by tomorrow he will be at hers," Mama and Gelmina were ready for inspection.

Within minutes of his first visit, people on the street, at the milk store, at the bread store, and at the fruit store talked about Poor Father Michele's house calls.

"Lina, what is your opinion? The church never misses the opportunity to ask for money, does it?"

"Ladies, empty bags do not stand up," the bread vendor said from behind the counter.

"Yes, it's true. I don't think they have much, Poor Father Michele," a sympathetic soul said. And that was that, because when all was said and done, people in Murano were gifted with a generous spirit, especially for the church, which they deemed a very important part of their lives. Therefore, they supported their priest even if they suspected that he had been elected by the communists and had reservations about his ability to be a good influence on their children.

Communism was just a word, an idea that never translated to anything other than a few social parties throughout the year. There was no doubt that the Catholic Church was the nucleus of the *Muranesi*'s everyday life.

In Murano, the children went to church to redeem their souls and to play with all of their friends. The girls joined the *Crociatine*, an association to honor Jesus through discipleship. They wore white uniforms with big, crimson crosses in the center, which they flaunted around the streets of Murano during the Holy Processions. All of the children went to catechism every Sunday. Some joined the Boy and Girl Scouts who met at the church during the week. Thus the reason why everyone felt compelled to support, within the boundaries of their financial possibilities, even Poor Father Michele, when he came around "to bless them all."

Together, with a young boy who held his pewter basket with the holy water in it, Poor Father Michele came up the stairs to our house. Panting, although only in his early fifties, he lifted his long black robe with one hand and held on to the rail with the other.

If he came in the afternoon after school, my siblings and I crowded at the entrance door behind Mama.

"Father Michele, come in," Mama said. "Come in please. I'm so glad you are here."

Meanwhile, Gelmina in the back, always ready to stir up trouble, turned her head away and made fun of him as she muttered through her teeth, "He needs to do a bit of hard labor." Then she walked away from the door before Mama gave her the stern look that struck each member of the family in turn when we did not behave.

Every year, as soon as he entered the house, Poor Father Michele asked us the same questions in his nasal drawl.

"*Come ti chiami?* How old are the children, Signora Teresa? What grades are they in? You have six children, don't you?"

Before Mama could answer, even if it was midday, he added, "Is Signor Nico at work?"

Afterward, we laughed with Gelmina about it, while Mama justified his questions by saying, "*Poveretto,* he doesn't know what to say."

Poor Father Michele, always an outsider even within the church realm where he should have been king. Always feeling inadequate. Never capable of relating his sentiments to his parishioners, he hid within the institution of the church, behind its walls, his own priestly attire, behind a mannerism which left people unaffected.

It did not matter. As a soldier of God, people respected his stand and treated him with a polite reverence, at least to his face. Thus, when he came to our house, every member of the family followed Poor Father Michele into each room and genuflected. He removed the silver rod from the small bucket, and sprinkled a few drops of holy water on the shiny floor and on our bowed heads. As he pronounced, "In the name of the Father, the Son, and the Holy Ghost," we all lifted our right hand, brought it up to our foreheads, to our chests, and to our shoulders. At the end of his visit, the Father walked into the kitchen, which he always blessed last. He sat on the edge of one of the wooden chairs and wiped the sweat off his forehead with a handkerchief not as white as it should have been—Gelmina's hawkish eyes noticed.

"Father Michele, would you like something to drink? A glass of *Marsala,* or an espresso coffee?" Mama said to him.

"No, thank you," he answered, his eyes scanning the room.

"Gelmina," Mama insisted. "Give Father Michele a glass of *Marsala* and some cookies."

Father Michele and his altar boy ate the homemade cookies. He drank the *Marsala* wine. The altar boy drank a glass of water. We children sat around the table and counted to ourselves the many black buttons that fastened his vest. In the end, we often argued that it was impossible to know how many buttons there were.

Before he left our house, Mama handed him a white envelope with a small donation, and off he went to the next house to bless the next walls, to eat more cookies and to drink more *Marsala*.

When we were sure he was down the stairs, we giggled.

"Did you see how hard he worked?" Gelmina complained. "I wish someone would give me an envelope when I go for a visit."

To that Mama would reply, "Gelmina, you know that he does not keep the money. You know that he sends most of the money to the Bishop and fixes the church."

Gelmina tightened her lips the way she always did when she did not agree with Mama, or when Poor Father Michele, his aunt and the condition of his house became the subject of our conversation.

"He and his sister could pull up their sleeves and work in their house like we do," Gelmina said, looking at us.

Father Michele and his sister did not have that kind of energy, and Papa said that Poor Father Michele had been chosen by the Communist Party because they wanted an ineffective priest around. I did not know what Papa meant by that, but I knew Mama and Papa were Christian Democrats, and that they made sure we learned that Communism shatters all of people's dreams, something very important to Papa.

Papa often cited an old proverb, "It's better to live a day as a lion than a hundred as a sheep, like the Communists."

To assert his point and to make sure everyone understood his message, Papa invited one of his friends and his wife for lunch when they came to Murano for a visit.

Papa's friend, Doctor Coppa, had visited Russia when no one else had. He and his wife talked about their experiences with the Russian officials who confiscated their luggage at the airport when they entered Russia and kept the suitcases for inspection for several days. Also, before the Russian Government allowed them to return to Italy, they sequestered their camera and the pictures they had taken on their trip.

I listened with admiration to Dr. Coppa's wife as her eyes sprang wide in amusement when she talked about the beauty of the Russian countryside and the imposing Red Square in Moscow. She nodded her head with disapproval when she recounted the Russian people's way of life. Through her stories, we vicariously experienced the beauty of a forbidden Russia, and the stark reality of the people who lived within its confines. Signora Coppa told us how she and her husband were never left on their own to stroll about throughout their whole trip.

"We had such an eerie feeling," she said. "Even when we were in our hotel room, we felt the need to whisper to each other."

"On the outside things seemed rather pleasant," Dr. Coppa explained. "But you could feel the tension of the dignitaries as they eyed and whispered to one another, and argued on what to do next. They often whisked us from one place to the next, pretending they were running out of time."

Dr. Coppa and his wife loved the Russian theater and the flawless performance of the Bolshoi Ballet. They enjoyed talking to the people they met and deemed them well read, even though books were scarce, found only on the black market.

Signora Coppa's neck veins puffed up when she said, "Imagine, Signora Teresa, people were forced to live in a commune. As many as three generations sleeping in the same room, and ten families using the same bathroom."

Perturbed, she added, "When I inquired about privacy, the mother of the Russian professor we had lunch with said, 'We elders take the children on picnics on Sundays so the younger generation can have privacy.'"

Privacy was not a big issue with us. It might have been strange for Dr. Coppa and his wife who did not have any children, but for a family of nine, privacy was something we knew nothing about, just like the Russians.

Every time Signora Coppa recounted how truly scared they had been when all of their possessions were confiscated for several days, and how she even thought that perhaps they would never see Italy again, she became very tense. To ease the tension, Papa told jokes about Italian Communists and their philosophy.

We children understood.

In silence, we concurred that Communism was not a desired form of government because Papa said so, and it would never have occurred to us to cross the threshold of the Communist Party Headquarters in Murano.

Even if Mama never said so, the Communist Headquarters was another area in Murano where Tina and I were not allowed to go because I knew that Mama, who was a devout Catholic, would have sent me to bed without dinner.

I would never have known where it was, but for an oval plaque with the communist symbol of a sickle and hammer on top of the brown double door. And I would never have crossed its threshold if my friend Laura had not invited me to go to the Annual Communist Beauty Contest on a sunny Sunday afternoon.

It was not a premeditated act. It was one of those unexpected moments in which one says "Yes," but should have said, "No, thank you. I have to visit my Aunt Claretta."

It was one of those moments when I was sorry the moment I uttered, "Yes," a decision I made in haste, one which labeled me for life.

After I went to the Communist Beauty Contest, Mama said to everyone that I was the most stubborn and independent member of the family and that if I wanted to do something, no one could stop me from doing it.

I thought it strange that one little escapade to the Communist Party Beauty Contest to watch my friend Laura would gain me the appellation "independent" for life.

Mama was dumb struck when, on her way home from a visit to Aunt Susi, a well-intentioned member of the Communist Party mentioned to her that I was at the Communist Party's celebration. Mama's first instinct was to change her route and pick me up at the celebration, but she would never have walked under the sickle and hammer. Humiliated by the discovery, she kept on walking home, livid.

It was not my fault if on the way to Aunt Claretta's house I met my friend Laura looking so pretty, dressed like a china doll, her long black hair rolled into little, bouncing curls touching her shoulders. She wore a frilly, pink dress with tiny yellow flowers all over the short, puffy sleeves, and a smile so wide and bright, I was sure Gelmina would have agreed that Laura's cheeks would hurt for days on end.

When I stopped to say how pretty Laura looked, Laura asked her Papa if I could go to the party with them. A prompt, enthusiastic "yes" made me feel special. And off we went.

We arrived in the courtyard. People stood around talking. The local band, several young boys and the maestro, the son of the post office clerk, were rehearsing. A man, wearing a red banner across his chest with yellow words written on it, kept trying the microphone, "*Uno, due . . . Uno due . . .Mi sentite?*" Colorful paper lanterns hung on nails on the red brick wall ready to be lit at sunset. A buzzing, a blurring of familiar faces, friends greeting each other, talking about their families, admiring each other's children, caused me to forget for a moment the feelings of misplacement. What I saw mimicked the church celebration held each year on the church grounds, only without Poor Father Michele. Long rectangular tables were set with colorful tablecloths, each place setting arranged in a straight line.

I sat next to Laura and her Papa.

Every time people approached our table to tell Laura how beautiful she looked, they would say with surprise, "Is this Nico's daughter?"

The ones who did not say that were told, "Look, this is Nico's daughter."

"Nico's daughter?"

"Oh, Nico's daughter."

No, Mama did not know how my guilty conscience gnawed at my stomach, how I wanted to run home, how I found the courage, at last, to say in a wee little voice to Signor Franco, while Laura and the other contestants were walking on the wooden platform up and down, stopping, crossing their legs as they curtsied, "Signor Franco, I have to go home."

Signor Franco was not ready to excuse me because he said, "The band is going to play, and Laura is going to sing her song *Mamma*, in a few minutes."

I did not want to listen to the song *Mamma*.

It was a popular song launched by Beniamino Gigli, an opera singer, an actor who played the main character in the movie *Mamma*. With throbbing passion, as he dedicated the song to all Italian mothers, when he sang it, the whole country, millions of Italians, cried their hearts out.

Mamma son tanto felice perche` ritorno da te...
Solo per te la mia canzone vola,

Sarai con me tu non sarai piu` sola...
Queste parole d'amore che mi sussurrano al cuore
Forse non s'usano piu`
Mamma, la mia canzone piu` bella sei tu,
Sei tu la vita, e nella vita non ti lascio mai piu`.

The song talks about a son who returns to live with his mother as he realizes she is the most important person in the world. He tells her that she will never be alone again.

The words of the song led the audience to a crescendo of sobbing when the man tells his mother that "she" is his best song, his whole life.

Trapped by the music, by the first few notes of the local band, by the crystalline sound of Laura's voice, I sat there, tears streaming down my rosy cheeks. I thought about my mama, feeling guilty, feeling love for her, stuffing the Saint Honoré cake down my throat, worrying about the consequences that lay ahead.

When I arrived home, I had to listen to a different song. The title was not *Mamma* but it was my mama's song, one she made up as I entered the kitchen where the whole family gathered, eating dinner. And as Mama escorted me to the bedroom she sang it to me.

Pointing her finger at the bed, she turned the light off, closed the door, and returned to the kitchen where I heard her say, "*Mamma mia*, what am I going to do with that girl. She is so stubborn and independent."

I knew Mama would not bring up the subject of communism ever again, unless she saw the absolute necessity to do so.

Guitar Lessons

A few weeks before Christmas, I said, "Papa, I want to learn to play the guitar."

He said, "Don't worry Anna, I'm going to find you a teacher."

The music teacher, a forty-five-year-old single man who lived with his old aunt because his parents were both dead, showed up at our door a week later, on a Friday evening, one hour before dinner so that, Papa said, "After the lesson he can eat with us."

Gidio rang the doorbell, and when Mama opened the door, he said, "*Ciao*, Signora Teresa." Then, he lifted his hand, brushing it back and forth across his bald-head.

Mama smiled at him and beckoned him to come in.

He walked into the kitchen and extended his right hand towards me. His unkempt countenance, and his attire that he wore with nonchalance, let you know that you were dealing either with a tramp, or with an eccentric. Underneath his open beige jacket, he wore a faded woolen sweater with several small holes for "decoration," he said. The white shirt-sleeves that hung out of his jacket were missing two buttons.

Gidio was an established artist who had won many accolades for his paintings. All the newspapers talked about him, about his talent, about his success as a modern painter. He painted geometric scenes of a resplendent sun shining on boats floating on the water, in bright hues of reds, oranges, yellows and greens. He was also a composer and an entertainer. Gidio and his friends performed, like Papa during his youth, at the annual church celebration.

Gidio made himself comfortable and sat in Papa's chair, "the throne," as he had baptized it. He crossed his legs, opened a small music book, placing it in front of me, and started teaching me a few notes. To test me, he asked me to play Antonio's guitar.

The extent of my musical experience had been to hold Antonio's guitar for a few minutes and pretend to strum it with my fingers. Gidio appeared surprised at how clumsy I was, but he did not say anything. As I moved my fingers from one position to the next, he tapped his right hand on the table to emphasize rhythm.

I dropped the guitar a couple of times, and as I stooped to pick it up, I bumped my head against Gidio's who laughed and muttered something I did not quite understand. I managed to break one string as a strident and screeching sound ballooned to the ceiling.

I was not having fun.

I did not know why I had asked Papa for guitar lessons and wished with all my heart for the hour to end soon. I wanted to run out of the house. I wanted. . .

The hour over, Gidio talked with my brothers and sisters as they came in for dinner.

Mama was preparing dinner while Gelmina and Gabri were setting the table. Gidio walked towards the kitchen stove and pulled the cover away from the frying pan. He told Mama something and she laughed. Mama took the lid away from him and put it back on the pot. When Gidio told Mama he was going home, she asked Antonio to pour a glass of red wine for Gidio and assured him that Papa would be home soon.

At seven-thirty, Papa rang the doorbell. He entered with Aunt Susi who every Friday night came to have a fish dinner with us. After Papa hung his gray coat and his hat on the hall's metal hook, he came into the kitchen.

"Gidio, where is he? Mama?"

Papa stopped for a second to look around the room.

"How are you doing, Gidio?" Papa said. "Come, Gidio. *Bambini*, Susi, come and sit at the table."

We all sat. Mama and Gelmina served each of us a small portion of *Risotto di Calamari* in a soup bowl. The risotto, cooked in the black liquid that the *calamari* squirt at their foes when they detect danger, may look unappetizing to foreign eyes, but to a Venetian, it is a true delicacy.

We children gulped our food.

Gidio, amused by how fast we ate, looked at each of us then hid his head under his arms, pretending to guard his food with fearsome determination.

When Mama passed the fried prawns and the sardines to him, he declined. "Signora Teresa, let me finish my rice first, and then I'll have the rest."

"Please, Signor Gidio," Mama insisted, "Take some now. I am afraid there will not be anything left later on. In our family, the dish goes around only once."

"It's so nice to see children eat with gusto," Gidio said.

"You see, Signor Gidio," Mama said, "I never give the children snacks during the day because I want them to eat a good meal."

"Yes," Papa added, looking at Mama. "If you feed children good food, you do not have to spend money on doctors. All of our money is spent on food. Isn't it true, Teresa?"

"Look at your father." Aunt Susi said. "He gets such pleasure just talking about food."

Aunt Susi was stunning, even though she had a bump on the bridge of her nose. When young, she had many contenders wanting to marry her. But Aunt Susi never married. We did not know why, as she was private about her life. Mama said that when young, Aunt Susi was meticulous in everything she did, even in deciding what outfit to wear. If my grandmother asked Aunt Susi, "Can you please go across the bridge to buy some bread," Aunt Susi would run up the stairs into her bedroom, take off her housedress, try on all of her outfits, sometimes twice, sometimes three times. She observed her reflection in the mirror, making sure no creases or imperfections appeared. She washed her face with the white cotton cloth her mama had laid on the dresser next to the water basin in her bedroom. She stroked her long ebony hair a hundred times, and shaped her bangs to the side. By the time she walked down the steps with regal flair, so as not to disturb the flow of her dress, my grandmother had sent my mama to buy the bread and often Mama would have come back already.

That is why when we asked Mama why she thought Aunt Susi had never married, she answered, laughing, "If she took as much time deciding on a boyfriend as she took choosing a dress, you can imagine why she never got married."

Aunt Susi, Mama's sister, was always welcome in our house, and we in hers. She helped Mama sew our clothes and cut our hair, and like Papa, she introduced us to music, opera, ballet, and always talked about all of her excursions around Italy.

Aunt Susi was right. At the mere mention of food, papa's eyes sparkled with enthusiasm.

Papa asked Gidio if his paintings sold well, then said, "Gidio, did you see the art show in Venice? It is spectacular! Picasso and Van Gogh."

Aunt Susi thought the show worth seeing as well.

"I want to go and see the show," Gabri told Papa. "I'll take my brothers and sisters."

"You'll see how interesting the show is going to be. I'll take you on Sunday," Gabri reassured us.

Mama passed a bowl of fresh fruit around while we all sat and talked.

"How is school, children?" Gidio said. "Are you good students?"

We looked at him but said nothing.

"I got a four on my math test today," Pietro dared to announce.

Pietro knew it was better to get the news out in the open before someone else relayed it to Mama. And anyway, he knew that Papa would come to his defense.

"What, what did he say?" Papa said. Mama got up, and speaking close to Papa's ear, repeated what Pietro had said.

"Pietro, tomorrow get another four, and the two will make eight," Papa said. Gelmina and Aunt Susi shook their heads, while we all looked at Mama who was mortified by Papa's nonsensical utterances. We waited for Mama's reaction to Papa's words.

"Signor Gidio," Mama said. "Instead of scolding the children when they get bad grades, Nico makes jokes. I just want the children to realize how important a good education is."

Papa winked. He knew he was in trouble. We all knew Papa wished he could have gone to school for a formal education.

Too proud to admit in front of Gidio that something had been amiss in his life, Papa said, "Gidio, hard work is the best. If the children do not want to go to school, they can go to work. Hard work is healthy. It's good for the body and mind."

"Do not listen to him," Mama said. "Children, study hard, as hard as you can."

Before Gidio left, he gave me some homework, a series of exercises to practice with Antonio's guitar for the following week. However, my career as a guitar player ended before Christmas arrived, as I did not like to practice. Never again did I ask Papa for music lessons.

An Esteemed Institution

As Christmas drew closer, the nights grew longer, the air colder, the wind louder. As the wind swept away the dark clouds, and the fog took an occasional stroll, the nights became as clear as the wine glasses Mama placed on the table during the holidays. The sky shone brightly as myriads of little stars gleamed through the heavens. During the day, you could spy the clear outline of the Dolomites peering at you from afar. Often I stared at the mountains topped with white snow. I liked the snow!

I got up one morning, and Mama was reading the newspaper to Gelmina, a morning ritual that lasted for more than fifty years. First, she read all the sad events in people's lives.

"Man Drowned in the Lagoon," said one article. "Young, Sixteen Year Old Boy Killed in a Car Accident in Mestre," said another.

She perused each page, looking for familiar names to see if anyone she knew died so that a member of the family could go to the funeral or send a card.

I entered the kitchen, still wearing my flannel pajamas. I kissed Mama and Gelmina on the cheek. I helped myself to breakfast.

"Your Papa, Gabri, and Antonio left half an hour ago," Mama said.

I looked at the clock. It was seven-thirty. I was annoyed that I did not hear Gabri's six o'clock alarm and that Mamma and Gelmina did not wake me up. I realized there was no way I could meet Tina and walk with her to the boat station. I wanted her to come with me in the afternoon to Venice to buy a gift for Aunt Susi for Christmas with the money I had saved each week since early summer. I had seen the red pouch in Venice in a little shop by the Rialto Bridge. Red was Aunt Susi's favorite color.

"Mama," I said, "I'm going to Venice this afternoon after I do my homework. I want to buy a red wallet for Aunt Susi."

Mama reminded me that the public boats were not running on schedule because the A.C.T.V. employees had declared a strike.

"Oh, no," I said, disappointed. Then I realized I did not have to be in school on time. I whirled around the table flapping my arms and hands as in a swan's dance.

"I think it's going to snow this afternoon," Mama said. "The sky is so gray. The wind stung my face when I went outside this morning. Cover yourself well, when you go out, Anna, and come home early."

Mama knew, Gelmina knew, and I, of course, knew that I was going to Venice even though the transportation system would not run on time.

A few minutes later, Giuliana entered the kitchen still half asleep. As she rubbed her eyelids with her knuckles, trying to adjust to the light, I asked her, "Who is taking you to kindergarten this morning? Can I take you?"

Giuliana's eyes brightened as she perched on Papa's favorite chair, arms crossed in front of her, chin resting on them, searching for an explanation of why I had not gone to school at the regular time.

I loved taking Giuliana to kindergarten. In fact, I could not remember the last time I had been inside.

The kindergarten, a two story building which stands even now on *Fondamenta degli Angeli*—albeit, without the nuns in it—is surrounded by a large piece of land.

From the main entrance, a long corridor, the main artery of the house, led to the back where the kitchen and pantry were situated. The recreation room, the first room on the left side of the corridor, had a small theater hidden by two red velvet curtains. It stood empty until the children, prepped by Sister Clementina, performed for their parents at the end of the year. On the same side of the corridor were two large rooms. One room was the conference room with a huge table in the middle where the benefactors or regents gathered two times a year to discuss the budget. The other one, the *Madre* Superior's office, was decked with a portrait of the Pope, the Bishop, and other church officials who stared at you with dignity.

If you kept on walking, the aroma of the kitchen fused with that of the children's lavatories and bathrooms. Miniature toilets lined along the wall for the boys. Past the boys', another door opened to the girls'.

On the right side of the corridor, a circular stairway led up to the first floor to the nuns' quarters.

The *Asilo Infantile,* an esteemed institution in Murano, gave mothers a much-needed respite. Each morning, mothers entrusted their little ones to a platoon of nuns who governed the establishment with an iron fist. At eight-thirty a.m., the young mothers grasped their children's hands, and walked through the iron-gate and down the cemented path lined on each side by tall, red and white oleanders.

To act like perfect mothers, they claimed, "Oh, I brought my little Leonardo, but I will miss him terribly."

To give credence to their words, they lingered outside by the gate, and talked to each other about their precious ones. They stood on tiptoes and observed, over the plastered brick wall, their children talking, holding hands in a circle, singing songs, or jumping rope.

The front yard was divided into two distinct sections. The boys played on the right side, the girls on the left. The division sent a loud and clear message. When we went out to play, we chanted a mantra from each side of the flower partitions, just like the boys and girls had sung before us, *"Fioi e fie fa pecà. Fioi e fie fa pecà."* "Boys and girls together, sin."

The girls wore checkered red and white uniforms with white starched collars and red silk bows. The boys wore blue and white-checkered ones, white collars, and dark blue bows tied in the front.

Every night, at the kitchen sink, before she went to bed, Mama washed the one uniform each of us had. She got up early to iron them. By the time we left the house in the morning, Aunt Claretta said we looked like we just came out of a gift box, all nice and clean and starched up, ready to go rolling in the dirt.

On our first day back after summer vacation, as we entered the green gate and walked down the cemented pathway, Gelmina would say to us, "Watch out children. The nuns are experts in making you say exactly what they want you to tell them. *Si, si.* They are more skillful than the Gestapo during World War II."

Even before we left the house Gelmina warned us to be careful.

"Say yes and no to the nuns like a stupid person." We really did not know who the "stupid person" was, but we got the message.

Mama and Papa did not feel the same way as Gelmina. They nurtured a lot of respect for the nuns since some of them had attended to Mama and Papa. Like dear, old Sister Pacifica, who knew every inhabitant of Murano by their first name. She had followed, with interest, the various stages of their lives.

Mama and Papa loved and respected the Mother Superior. Even though at times we felt intimidated by her imposing demeanor, Mama said that the Mother Superior went out of her way to help families in need.

They thought highly of Sister Clementina, everybody's favorite nun. She looked so pretty when she walked down the long corridor singing like a canary, her black veil trailing behind her, dancing in the air. She made us sing in class while we sat at our desks. As we outlined the shape of an Easter dove, or Baby Jesus for Christmas, using a needle to punch holes into a colored, shiny paper, we opened our mouths and let the words and melody reach God because, "He likes music," Sister Clementina told us.

The three years I attended kindergarten were paved with small joys as well as sorrowful tears that I learned to wipe off and move on.

After we entered through the main front door, we were instructed to walk, in silence, down the long corridor in a straight line, along a narrow strip that extended two feet from the wall, boys on one side, girls on the other. Not an easy task when the boys teased us girls, and our volatile instincts sent us across the hall to hit them in the arm like a missile. Such action distressed the nuns to no end. For the most part, we ended up in the middle of the corridor tiptoeing next to Sister Agata. As she ushered us to the Mother Superior's office, we prayed to the Virgin Mary that the Sister would not detach our ears from our heads.

Most of all, we learned that if we didn't conform and behave according to the nuns' creed, or if we talked and laughed with our friends during Mass on Sunday, come Monday, Sister Agata would make us stand in the middle of the corridor in front of everybody, and smack us across the face with such energy that we would end up against the wall, crying. To console us, our friends would dig a hole in the ground and feed us the smallest rocks as a panacea. With much gratitude, we would swallow them as fast as we could and brag about how many we had ingested that day.

Mama did not approve of Sister Agata's mode of discipline but remained silent.

Gelmina, on the other hand, was very vocal about it, and with anger and disdain, she made sure we knew she was on our side.

Addressing Mama, she would say, "Did you hear what Sister Agata did to Anna? That nun is terrible. You can see from her face that she is *tremenda*. Stay away from her, Anna."

In Murano, people adopted a no-nonsense approach. What was right was what people said was right.

That is also how Papa learned. He learned a jarring lesson at a very early age, not from the nuns, but from his second grade teacher in the local public school.

Aunt Claretta told us that Papa had quicksilver in his legs when he was young. He was gifted with a tremendous spirit of adventure, which he exploited in the second grade. Not having any toys, he made swords with the small branches he found in the school yard. He constructed hats with old newspaper pages people discarded on the edge of the *fondamenta* along the canal. He took his self-made toys to class and hid them under his desk. When the teacher taught something he did not like, he would distribute his hand-made crafts to all his friends, causing a lot of friendly fights and much chaos in the classroom.

Aunt Claretta told us that in desperation my grandmother kept repeating, "I do not know what's in his head. I know someday they will bring Nico home in a coffin if he doesn't shape up."

Her prediction almost came true. The teacher did bring Papa home one day after he played dead for a whole afternoon. To fix a pipe, a few workers had dug a huge hole in the schoolyard. On a whim, to show his friends that he could play dead, Papa lifted the wooden planks the workers had placed on top of the hole, plunged himself inside the small trench, made his friends swear to secrecy and told them to place the wooden planks back. On his back, he waited.

His poor teacher went insane looking for him. So did the school dignitaries while his loyal friends watched in silence. When they finally discovered Papa's hideout, his teacher took him home, without a word.

The teacher called Grandmother from the street.

Grandmother poked her head out of the window.

"*Maria Santissima*, Signora. What did he do today?" Grandmother said as she ran down the three flights of stairs, into the *calle*.

"Here is his second grade diploma," the teacher told Grandmother. "Do not send him to school tomorrow or ever again." To let Grandmother know she meant it, the teacher pointed at Papa, moving her finger back and forth, right, left, right, left, right and left.

"I have never met anyone so mischievous in my whole life," she hollered. With an angelic expression on his face, Papa watched his mother as he scratched the dirt with one foot. While a few heads peeked through the curtains of nearby apartments, Grandmother stood in the middle of the street speechless, diploma in her hand. When Papa's teacher turned around and marched back to school, one of the neighbors came out for a few seconds to console Grandmother while she cried. Papa cried a little, too.

The following day, Grandmother dragged Papa to the shoemaker in *Fondamenta dei Vetrai*. First, she stopped by the church. She shed a few more tears in front of the Virgin Mary while Papa buried his face in the black shawl that hung from his mother's shoulder. Grandmother made the sign of the cross and said a few Hail Marys. She explained her situation to the Virgin Mary, certain that the Virgin would listen to her.

Revitalized, Grandmother marched across the *Ponte San Pietro Martire*, and determined to make use of all of her holy connections, she rang the doorbell of the rectory, adamant to find little Nico a job. Any job. Because if anyone in Murano was looking for a job for a mischievous son or daughter, or a favor, that is what people did. First they prayed, then they rang the doorbell of the rectory.

Holding Papa by the hand, Grandmother trailed behind the priest and waited outside the shoemaker's shop. The Reverend went inside to barter for Papa's job. One eye on the shoemaker, the owner of the shop, one on the priest, one ear outside, one listening to what was said on the inside, when Grandmother saw the shoemaker shake his head, uncertain if to give

Papa a job, she leaned in the door and begged, " Vittorio, please, take Nico as an apprentice. We do not want any money. We just want him off the street."

The shoemaker looked at the priest, at Grandmother, at the priest again, sighed, and then nodded his head. He handed Papa a piece of an old sole, a hammer and a few short, tiny nails, and ordered him to pound as hard as he could on the old sole he placed on the steel form. Thus seven-year-old Nico began his multi-flavored career.

To make us laugh, Aunt Claretta said that if Grandmother could string into a necklace all the tears she shed for Papa, she would have the longest necklace in the universe.

When Aunt Claretta told us the story of when Papa became a young adult, and how he looked at his canvas sideways, upside down, and how he finally decided to paint on it his own unique design with many stars and flowers, she reminded us about Papa's resilient spirit.

She rumbled about the times Papa stepped over the lines in school. She told us how often he fell in the canal, and how his knees were always bruised. Adding, at the end of the story that by the time Papa was fifteen, so many people in Murano had instructed him on what to do that he finally learned to walk, stroll, jump, and hop around Murano with his eyes shut.

I understood what Aunt Claretta meant because when I met Sister Pacifica on the street, and she felt like talking, she said, "Your Papa was a *biricchino* when young. He gave your grandmother a lot of gray hair. We were all worried about him. But look at him now. You have such a nice Papa."

Talking to Sister Pacifica always brought fragments of my own kindergarten years to mind. Like the time I snuck into Sister Clementina's classroom with Gabri on the first day back after summer vacation. Smiling, standing by her desk on top of the wooden platform, Sister Clementina waited in her classroom for all of the children to come in. Hands folded, she observed each child as he entered in single file. She smiled as she saw me, but said nothing and began her lesson.

Mama said Sister Clementina was her favorite nun because she had an infectious laugh, and could find humor in situations instead of turning them into Great Inquisitions. I knew what Mama was alluding to. She was referring to the day when I heard Gabri tell Sister Clementina about her visit to the Pope. For when Sister Clementina asked the children to share what they had done during the summer, since no one raised their hands, Sister Clementina said, "Come, Gabri. Stand here by me and tell everyone what you and your family did this summer."

"I went to see the Holy Eminence, the Pope, with my whole family," Gabri said with reverence in her voice as she twirled her long braid with her right hand, and genuflected when she went by the Sister.

Everyone's ears perked up.

Sister Clementina's eyes widened as she said, "To see the Pope!"

To catch a fragment of His Holiness, she put one hand on Gabri's shoulder and probed Gabri to tell everyone the details of her audience with the Pope. Sister Clementina cheered Gabri into finishing the story, then took Gabri to the Mother Superior who listened, as well, with interest.

Gabri gave a detailed account about how a priest with many rings on his fingers, a pair of black shoes with tiny buttons, a black vestment that touched the floor with a large red sash around the waist, took our whole family into a room painted with frescos, and made us wait there for a long time. Together with a large crowd of the faithful, we waited until a nun escorted everyone, a few people at a time, to a different room where the Pope sat on his throne ready to bless us all.

Prior to our audience with the Pope, Gabri said a nun came to tell us that we needed to put scarves on our heads. Gabri said that our family stood for hours in a single, straight line, waiting, and that Papa was the first one in line. Mama, who was wearing a white lace veil on her head that her own mama had made when she had gone to visit the Pope many years before, held little Margherita in her lap. Next, came Gabri and Antonio, me, and even Gelmina. When we entered the room, we lowered our heads, genuflected in front of the Pope. We stood immobile for a few seconds until he put his hand on our heads. We kissed his other hand several times in the exact spot where he had a fancy, huge ring.

Gabri went on to explain that the Pope said in Latin to each of us, "Pax Tecum," and when Gelmina genuflected in front of him, he said, "My Child, get up."

"What did your mother say, Gabri," Sister Clementina interrupted.

"My mama cried. Even my papa had tears in his eyes."

"And Gelmina? What was it like for Gelmina to have had an audience with *Sua Eminenza,* the Pope," asked Sister Clementina.

"Gelmina was red in the face when the Pope put his hand on her shoulder."

Both sisters brought Gabri into the kitchen so she could retell her story to the other nuns.

At four o'clock in the afternoon, Sister Clementina waited for Mama at the main entrance, and when she saw Mama approaching, she left us children with Sister Pacifica.

"Signora Teresa," she said, a glow in her eyes, "what an honor it must have been to have had an audience with the Pope."

At the word "Pope," two ladies on the right side of Mama stopped, turned their heads and said, "The Pope? We did not know you went to see the Pope, Teresa."

Mama stopped. Puzzled, she said to Sister Clementina, "The Pope?" Her face flushed. She lowered her eyelids.

It was a good thing Sister Clementina was standing in front of Mama and not Sister Agata. Before Mama had time to ask for an explanation, Sister Clementina began to laugh. She laughed so hard, her chest moved under her thick, black vest. Mama, the two ladies who had stopped to hear some details of Gabri's trip, and the ladies who were just going by and who heard the tail end of the conversation, began to laugh as well.

"Oh, Gabri has such a wonderful imagination," Sister Clementina said. And that was that. She asked no further questions, but said to Mama, "Signora Teresa, come and collect your children. See you tomorrow."

Mama did not talk all the way home, but we knew something was brewing because she was conversing with herself. She kept her eyes on the cobblestones and had to force herself to say hello to people when they called out to her and said, "*Ciao,* Teresa."

At home, Mama said that she had never been so embarrassed in her entire life. She said that Gabri should never have lied because liars are worse than thieves.

She said, "Gabri, what possessed you to tell Sister that you went to see the Pope?"

Gabri answered as if it were not her fault at all. "The Sister gave me the third degree."

We all turned to look at Gelmina.

We should have known. Mama should have known that it was Gelmina's fault because before she dropped us off at the *Asilo Infantile*, she muttered to herself as she accompanied us down the cement path, "Look at the sisters, they are all ready to give you the third degree."

In fact, it was Great Aunt Nice who had visited the Pope. It was Great Aunt Nice who told everyone who came to her house about her audience with the Pope down to the last minute detail. It must have impressed Gabri because she repeated each account of Great Aunt Nice's story, even mimicking her enthusiasm.

Mama in the end had to laugh, but not before she set everyone straight, and even called on Papa to reprimand Gabri.

"Gabri," Papa said, "you must not say things that are not true."

"Mama, some day we are going to take the children to see the Pope," he added. "Yes, the Pope. Great man, the Pope."

To receive a blessing from the Pope, to have a personal audience with him, must have been another one of Papa's dreams.

A Trip to Venice

After lunch, on that same day I took Giuliana to kindergarten, I went as usual to Signora Maria's. Around four-thirty, I bid goodbye to everyone. Even if the public boats were on strike, I was determined to go to Venice to purchase a small wallet for my Aunt Susi. On the way, I decided to stop by Tina's house to see if she would accompany me. All bundled up in my camel coat, with a green woolen scarf around my neck, I smelled the fresh air, looked at the stark, gray sky, and noticed the first sign of snow falling on the ground.

"It's snowing," the lady walking in front of me said to her husband. "Didn't I tell you that it would snow today?"

"I knew that," her husband answered. "I felt it in the air for the last few days. I knew it would snow before Christmas. Why do you think I brought my umbrella with me?" The man raised his black umbrella and opened it to protect himself and his wife from the few snow-flakes that were dancing and dashing through the sky.

At four-thirty, it was getting dark outside. I did not have an umbrella, and did not care if the snowflakes fell on my face and on my coat. I liked it when I opened my mouth and the flakes fell on my tongue. I imagined that they were like the manna God had sent to the Jewish people.

I turned the corner onto *Fondamenta Degli Angeli*. The snowflakes frolicked in all directions. They looked like lost delicate, white petals in an errant search for spring, looking for a peaceful place in which to settle. One snowflake fell on the tip of my nose. I closed one eye so I could focus on the snowflake before it dissolved on my skin. Even though I despised the cold, and longed all winter for one of those hot summer days when the sun kissed my face and warmed my body for days on end, I loved the snow. I hurried towards Tina's house to share this special moment with her.

As I walked past the *Asilo Infantile*, Sister Clementina was closing the gate.

"Hi, Marchini. The snow, we have snow," she said as she turned and ran down the cemented path.

"Hi, *Madre* Clementina," I said, as I strained my eyes to see if Davide appeared in sight. I had hoped to meet Davide so that I could say to him, "Do you like the snow? It's so wonderful."

I wanted to tell him how the snow made my heart happy as if it were spring. How it made me think of God. How I wanted to have a snowball fight with all of our friends. How I wanted to run home and watch the snow with my Papa through the kitchen window like we had done when I was younger.

Tina was not at home, and when I went by Davide's uncle's shop, I did not see him either. For days, now, I kept mulling over the words, "He likes you." Tina had not said, "I think he likes you." She had said, "He likes you," with a mischievous expression on her face that told me something was amiss. For sure, there was a big difference. Had she said, "I think. . .he likes you," I would probably not have given the words a second thought, and just would have been happy that Tina said that. And my other friends assured me that they were sure Davide liked me. Of course, it could have been that my mind was working overtime and that I was reading into their comments what I wished would happen.

Also, a few days earlier, Davide and I walked up and down *Fondamenta Cavour* near the Glass Museum, and sat together in the freezing cold, on the white edge of the *fondamenta*. We watched the motor boats swish by and observed the *gondoliere* in his *gondola* who, rain or shine, transported passengers from one side of the *fondamenta* to the other. We had talked about all of our friends, and when I said, "I have to go home now," he got up and walked me to my doorstep.

However, I could not forget that when we asked Davide who he liked best, he had chosen to omit my name. Now I was thinking that perhaps he liked me even then, but had not been ready to share that information with anyone. And he had kissed Emilia, and just thinking about it, my body felt like sinking in the deep canal's water.

There were days, like today, when he did not show up at Signora Maria's house for his homework, and I conjured up all kinds of situations as to why he had not come.

I couldn't see the whole picture.

I went about all day hoping for a sign, for a hint that could enlighten me on his feelings. I plucked hundreds of petals from tall, white daisies I found in the recesses of my mind. One by one, I pulled each delicate petal off, thinking, "He loves me. . .he loves me not. . .He loves me. . .He loves me not."

As I walked towards the boat station, all wrapped up in my own thoughts, I met Cousin Silvana and Aunt Claretta who asked, "*Bambina*, where are you going in this weather?"

When I said I was heading for Venice, Aunt Claretta gave me a little sermon of why I should go home instead because of the weather, because of the strike and because of the darkness of the night.

Aunt Claretta said what she always said when we met on the *fondamenta*, "You are so beautiful! Look, Silvana, she looks just like me when I was young."

Just about the same words everybody on the island said to me.

People always reminded me that I looked just like Aunt Claretta, which was not so bad, as Aunt Claretta was an attractive woman, but for the purple cheeks and double chin that now folded into her neck, making it disappear. My cheeks were already purple, as for my neck, I had a short neck, but it still looked like a neck should. I feared, though, that when I got older, just like Aunt Claretta's neck, it probably would disappear behind dangling, flapping skin.

I said good-bye to Aunt Claretta and to Cousin Silvana, and trotted a little faster. Many people were outside in the freezing air talking to each other, scurrying from shop to shop. However, people dwindled their number when I approached the *Colonna*. A few commuters were waiting for the boat to come, but not as many as usual, for sensible people, Mama would have said, stayed home in this kind of weather.

After a ten-minute wait, I embarked and went to sit inside the *vaporetto*. I pressed my nose against the window, and through the faint glow of the yellow lights situated on each side of the public boat, I observed the snow disappearing into the menacing waves. The *vaporetto* did not stop at the cemetery, but swished on to Venice. No one had requested to stop at the cemetery, and there was no "frozen" monk waiting to be picked up.

Fondamente Nuove was the first stop, and during a strike, it was the last one as well. If one needed to go on to the train station, one had to walk all the way to the other side of Venice, to the *Ferrovia* to catch the train, or to the *Piazzale Roma* to catch the bus. But, as the shop was near the *Rialto*, a ten minute walk, I was not concerned whether the public boats went any further.

I disembarked. A gush of wind stirred me towards *Calle Del Fumo*. The small tiny flakes changed into heavy clumps of huge, swirling cotton balls, and began to stick to the ground, to the rooftops, to the empty flower pots in windowsills, and to the corners of the entrance doors. I looked down at my clumsy, leather shoes. I traced the various footprints, at times sinking my feet firmly within their outlines, at times thrusting my shoes in the untouched cushion of chalky snow. I raised my lapel and wrapped my wool scarf around it to protect my throat. I moved forward in the freezing weather, my head uncovered, my hair wet from the falling snow, my kinky ringlets framing my forehead.

It was lovely, I thought, to look at the snowflakes through the reflections of the artificial light emanating from the windows of the various shops. I kept on walking, looking all around, looking up, catching with my gloved-hands a snowflake here and there, even running after them. Transported by the gust of wind, which impelled my body from the back, my feet almost did not touch the ground. My heart felt light.

Snow did not fall every day in Venice and the nearby islands. In fact, it was a rarity. Perhaps we would experience the falling snow a couple of days throughout the winter months, and even at that, most of the time it was a wet snow that did not stick to the ground but became muddy before anyone could enjoy the purity of its color.

As I walked, I noticed a short figure coming towards me, head buried in the lapel of a gray, tweed woolen coat, oblivious to what was happening around him.

"Hi, Davide," I said, as I pushed my hair back. "What are you doing here?"

A surprised Davide smiled as he said, "I'm running home. I'm freezing to death."

"But the snow…Don't you like the snow? It's so beautiful," I said.

"I'm going to *Rialto*. Come, please come."

"I went shopping with my father," he said. "I was freezing. He was not too happy when I left him. If he sees me walking around Venice, he'll kill me."

"Come on, we'll walk fast." As I said that, Davide turned around, and we walked to *Rialto*, into the shop where I purchased the small wallet for Aunt Susi.

On the way back to Murano, the wind bellowed with fury. With a steady crescendo, the wind had raised its pitch with the vicissitude of a symphonic poem in which the snow danced, erratically through the air, not really sure where to land.

"*Mamma mia*, I can hardly breathe," I uttered, as Davide pulling me by the arm, led me to shelter within the recess of the entrance door of a *pasticceria*.

For a few minutes, we watched a passerby juggle with his umbrella, and running after it when it fell on the floor scurrying away in the opposite direction. We laughed at each other, at our soaking hair, and at our frozen feet. Our eyes furtively locked, but only for an instant. Then we looked elsewhere, at the street, at the inside of the *pasticceria* crowded with people standing and drinking a piping hot *puncetto*, an *espresso coffee*, a *cappuccino*.

"Would you like something hot?" Davide said, after a few minutes.

"Yes, a cappuccino," I said.

Inside of the *Pasticceria*, everyone was talking about the weather conditions, guessing how many days they would have to endure such treacherous inconveniences. With reassurance, they convinced and pacified each other that the snowstorm soon would stop. Some of us, thinking with a romantic heart, that, if this weather endured, we would have snow on Christmas Eve, and we would have to slosh through the white carpet to Midnight Mass.

Davide and I drank our *cappuccino* in silence. The colorful candy boxes displayed on top of the counter, the various pastries of all shapes and forms, the long rows of traditional Christmas *panettone*, the scent of baked goods, the warmth of the people standing around articulating their thoughts, made me feel quite comfortable.

"Yes, I like Christmas," I said to Davide as if answering a question. "I like our relatives coming over. My Papa sings all day long on Christmas. Well, not really. He sings la, la, la, la. He walks around the house singing la, la, la, while Mama and Gelmina do all the work."

I paused for a few minutes, then said, "I love my Papa. He is great."

"My relatives do not come over because they live with us, already." Davide said.

"I know," I said.

I looked outside again.

"Davide, do you want to go?"

"Brrrrr. I'm going to freeze tonight. This is how cold my bedroom gets. We call it Siberia," he said as we stepped into the snow.

We walked in silence.

It would have been nice to go by Signora Maria's house to see if our friends were still there and invite them to step outside into *Campo San Bernardo* for a snow fight.

"*Permesso, permesso, permesso.*" Several boys, who were holding huge black umbrellas up high so that they would not poke us in the eyes, wanted to go by. Davide and I stepped to the side for a moment and saw that two of the young men were Tina's neighbors. I came face to face with one of Papa's workers walking in the opposite direction. He did not stop but told us to run if we wanted to catch the boat that had just docked at *Fondamente Nuove*. I turned my head towards Davide, and we shot ahead like two motor boats running a race. We did not stop till we stepped onto the boat.

In Murano, I met Papa who was going home from work. He kept on walking as he passed us, but said, "Anna, come home soon."

With a gesture of his hand, bringing it to his temple, as if he were saluting a general, Papa looked in Davide's direction and waved. He had said to go home soon. It was not an order, as Papa never gave orders. He always left the door open for us to use our own judgment, our common sense.

Of course, at that particular moment, there was no way I could have used my common sense. Everyone in Murano knew that when you let your heart guide you, common sense walks out of the window and disappears into the *fondamenta*. Strange, though, how there was so much common sense walking around. When it was to judge others, to make crucial decisions for someone else's life, all of the common sense experts would declare, "That girl seems to lack common sense."

Papa thought I had common sense, and I thought I was gifted with common sense. Especially, when some of my friends asked me for advice. Or when I appointed myself "judge" and tried to mediate a fight or an argument. On those occasions, no gossamer substance filmed my eyes, and I could see the whole picture as if I were looking through the mirrors in Papa's factory.

But in matters of love, there was something lacking in my common sense. It could be that I was positive of my feelings for Davide but did not know anything about his. So I just played the guessing game, which did not require any common sense at all. At times, I felt he liked me. However, I could not be sure. As far as I could see, he was not going to volunteer the information. Coming from a third party, it was not the same as if he had said three simple words, "I like you." Or even the bigger and better words, that seemed rather preposterous for a twelve year old to utter, but that would have solved my dilemma once and for all. Because, when I felt foolish using the word love, I reminded myself that Mama had fallen in love with Papa at thirteen, so there probably was nothing ridiculous about falling in love at twelve.

Uncle Ruggero fell in love with his wife in grade school. He noticed Aunt Lina entering the school courtyard all starched up in her black uniform with a white collar and a red silk bow in the front. He stared at her in wonder like one would a young princess. While all the boys thrashed around in the main school hall just to show off, Uncle Ruggero eyed her from a distance, like Papa did with Mama, till they both were old enough to talk about marriage.

Also, during my Italian literature class, my teacher had said that Dante had fallen in love with Beatrice at age nine, the first time he saw her, and immanently loved her till he died.

I did not want to wait ten years like Mama and Aunt Lina did, or till after I died, like Beatrice, before I found out if Davide liked me. A little reassurance from Davide, I thought, would have been a good thing.

"Do you want to go to Signora Maria's to get your books before you go home?" Davide said as we stepped onto *Ponte Lungo*.

"Yes, are you coming?"

"I might as well. I'm soaking wet already."

"I hope Tina and Aldo are still there. Perhaps we can have a snowball fight."

"The boys against the girls," he said.

Signora Maria's house was still crowded with students.

When we entered, Signora Maria said, "Look at you two. You are all wet. Where have you been? *Mamma Mia,* go home and change before you catch a cold."

"We went to Venice," I said.

I walked through the kitchen into the back room.

"Are Tina and Aldo still here?" I said. "Does anyone want to come and have a snowball fight?"

Everyone got up: Tina, Aldo, Sele, and our other friends. We walked out of Signora Maria's house as she said with approval, "You are going to have a snowball fight."

"And you, why aren't you going?" she said in a voice of command, addressing the few students sitting next to her in the dining room.

Tina and I ran ahead, and before anyone was ready, we shouted, "Boys against girls." We bent over to gather some snow and threw it right smack into Aldo's and Davide's faces.

A passerby yelled several times, "Be careful, be careful, be careful not to fall and break your legs."

As if common sense was something we needed right at that particular moment when we were having so much fun. Just when Davide grabbed a handful of snow and was shoving it in my mouth, holding on to my arm so I would not escape. When Tina and Sele ran after Aldo, and the other boys stood with snowballs in their hands waiting for the right moment to throw them.

We were having a good time.

Leaning against the wall, Signora Maria watched, laughing like a child.

When it was time to go home, in the euphoria of the evening, Davide said to me, "I'll walk you home."

Reading so much into that simple sentence, forgetting that I was gifted with much common sense, I whispered hoping he would not hear me, "Do you like me?"

He did not answer, but asked instead, "Sunday, are you coming to Renzo's house to dance?"

I nodded.

"See you tomorrow," he said.

I stood for a few moments at my front door watching Davide walk away, my books in one arm, and the small package with Aunt Susi's wallet in the other till the door clicked open.

What's Right is Right

"Christmas is practically around the corner," Mama said to me when I asked how many days were left before we could buy the Christmas tree.

Of course, I knew very well that tradition dictated we buy the tree on Christmas Eve Day. I wanted the biggest and the best tree Papa could buy. That is all I asked for Christmas, a huge tree so that the house would smell of pine whose scent would make me feel as if I were out walking among the pine trees in Uncle Paolo's Mountains. That is what Uncle said when he came over with Aunt Lora for lunch on Christmas day.

"*Mmmmm, che buon profumo*. I feel as if I'm roaming around my mountains. Where did you buy this tree?" Uncle Paolo said as he entered our living room.

"My mountains," that is what he called the Dolomites. He always said it with nostalgia and a twinkle in his eyes, and displayed so much emotion as if he were ready to cry.

Every year, we set up the tree in the living room, so that in the evening, after our Christmas Eve dinner, we could decorate it with chocolate ornaments my youngest brother Pietro ate when no one was looking.

Under the tree we placed the nativity set, so Pietro, just to be mischievous, could wrap all of the holy figures, as well as the shepherds, in foil and hide them till Christmas morning, till Jesus' birth.

I couldn't wait to go to church on Christmas Eve, sit with my family near my friend Tina, see Davide and Aldo, and sing the *Messa Solenne* in Latin with the whole congregation.

I loved the Christmas service. It was such a contrast to the place where Jesus was born. I always felt it to be a true paradox, to celebrate with such pomposity the life of a man who advocated simplicity and poverty. But the congregation, the priests in their gold and red garments, the lights glowing from the old Venetian chandeliers, the warmth from the few portable stoves lit especially for the occasion, and the smiles on people's faces, reassured me that it was the right thing to do.

I supposed the priest thought just like Mama. Even though he was frugal during the year, on a special occasion such as Christmas, he splurged and went out of his way to make sure his parishioners understood the importance of being together, of listening to the story of Jesus' birth over and over again.

Traditions were very important.

Every year on Christmas morning, we went to see all our relatives to wish them Merry Christmas. We also went to the *Colonna* with cousin Adriana, Uncle Ruggero's daughter, to wait for Uncle's best friend, the one who carried Uncle in a wheelbarrow after the war. He and his wife, who owned a toy store, brought a toy to each of us children.

At one o'clock in the afternoon, after Mama and Gelmina cleaned, cooked, and set a special table, all of our relatives came over for lunch.

We sat around the table. After lunch, when Aunt Claretta came, she sat on the opposite side of Aunt Lora, but made sure never to miss Christmas because Christmas was for family, and the family got together no matter what.

With merriment we ate, talked and often sang, but most of all we listened to many beautiful stories over and over.

Like the ones Papa told to Antonio, Gabri and me while we were helping him at his new factory, after the schism of his partnership with Uncle Nano.

I remember the day I came home and heard Mama say, "Nicolò, Claretta is your sister. What is going to happen to our family?"

Mama had worried that day when Papa announced he wanted out of the partnership with his brother-in-law, Uncle Nano.

When Mama repeated to him, "Claretta is your sister," Papa sat, with his arms on the table, hands folded onto each other, and stared at the sky through the kitchen window. He moved his head in assent, as he repeated under his breath, "My sister, yes, my sister. She has nothing to do with this. It's not right. It's not right."

"Nicolò, are you sure you want to take this step all on your own? The children are so little," she added with trepidation in her voice. "What if the new company fails? How will we feed the children? Your brothers are right. You should just stay. Stay put for a while longer, until the children are grown."

While Mama and Papa had this conversation, we children listened, trying to be invisible.

"It's not right that Remigio is robbing us blind, and Nano does not want to acknowledge it."

"Everyone knows that he is stealing our gold leaf booklets," Papa added with sadness in his voice. "Everyone is talking about it at the factory. Nano is the only one who does not want to believe it. They are best friends."

Every day for some time, Remigio, the director of Papa and Uncle Nano's glass factory, filled his lunch bag with gold leaf booklets, the ones they used with the molten glass to fuse shiny sparkles into it. Word went around that he took, as well, anything that he could put in his briefcase. The workers told Papa things they would never have said to Uncle Nano.

"Signor Nico, the *direttore* is robbing you blind. He records three gold books for a glass object, while in reality he only uses one. The other two, he puts in his pocket."

People joked that Remigio was starting his own small company with Uncle Nano's and Papa's money. Not that the factory was thriving. Papa and Uncle Nano had expanded their small mirrors *laboratorio*—that could not feed us all—into a factory of various buildings with many more employees. This led to more expenses, thus they were still struggling to get their heads above water, after several years.

After some inquiries about Remigio, Papa confronted Uncle Nano, who doggedly rejected the information.

When Papa said, "I cannot be your partner if we keep Remigio," not a muscle on Uncle's face twitched. What twitched was Papa and Mama's hearts.

Both sat at the kitchen table. Mama reminded Papa that a break in the partnership would mean a break with the family; Papa, pensive, trying to decide which course to take.

"Nano is so naive! He just cannot conceive his best friend cheating on him. It's not right. It's just not right," Papa repeated over and over, as if to himself.

After a while, Papa explained to Mama that he would open a small company in one of the three-story buildings adjacent to the factory. He said he was going to make mirrors as he had done before and would find a friend to help him assemble them.

Papa looked at us children, and said in a proud tone, "My children are going to help me." He smiled, then added, "We have nothing to worry about. God will take care of us. He always does."

Both Mama and Papa agonized over their decision. Mama relented. They called a mediator for the division of the business. A court day was set.

My siblings and I worried about what to do when we met Uncle Nano and Aunt Claretta on the street. We worried about missing Sunday dinners at their house where we went, one or two at a time, to eat Aunt Claretta's pasta with ragu, which was much tastier than Mama's. We worried that we could not see Cousin Silvana anymore, that she would not come to sleep at our house, stinky feet and all, on Saturday nights when Uncle and Aunty went out with Remigio and his wife. We worried that cousin Silvana could not go with us to Uncle Paolo's mountains during the summer. And we worried that Aunty would not give us the fifteen lire to go to the movies with our friends on Sunday afternoons.

We children would miss the sound of Aunt Claretta's voice calling us from the front door of her third floor apartment. She always waited for us to climb the three flights of stairs, covered with Titian red carpet. We would race up, skipping a few steps at a time, stomachs growling, our mouths watering from the smell of food that came from her kitchen.

"*Bambini, Bambini,* you are here," Aunty would say. "Who came today? Look, Nano, how beautiful they are. Look what beautiful red cheeks they have. Look how tall they are. I'm so glad you are here. Come, come inside."

She embraced us, kissed us with her bright red lips which left a mark on our faces, and repeated in her Venetian dialect, "*Varda che beli che I ze!*"

Uncle Nano, slouched in his favorite green chair reading the daily newspaper, *Gazzettino,* smiled at us and kissed us back when we stooped to kiss him. We all sat at the dining room table decorated with a colorful bowl of fruit as a centerpiece, and crystal glasses, mineral water, and a bottle of genuine country wine.

"Do you want to drink wine," Aunt Claretta asked us before she sat at the table.

We nodded our heads as she poured a glass full of water with a few drops of red wine in it.

"Look, look, how much wine I gave you. Your head is going to spin. Be careful not to fall in the water on your way home. Make sure you don't walk on the edge of the *fondamenta,*" she said as she pointed her index finger to the glasses.

Aunt Claretta laughed. She filled our dishes with her delicious pasta, and after we ate all of it, she refilled the dishes with a second helping.

We children worried. But there was nothing to worry about, as Papa, the thinker in the family, had worked out the whole thing in his head.

Just a few days after he left the factory, our family gathered together to clean the dilapidated building that was going to be Papa's new business location. We carried the machinery and the various supplies up and down the stairs, trying not to trip on the uneven floor. We pretended to look enthusiastic, to cheer up Mama whose heart was crying.

"*Bambini,* tomorrow is Sunday," Papa said as if it were the most natural thing to say. "Do not forget to go over to Aunt Claretta and Uncle Nano's."

Antonio and I went. We rang the doorbell, ran up the steps, skipping a few steps at a time, and sniffed the *ragù* sauce. We listened for any change in Aunt Claretta's voice, and watched her as she kissed and loved us, as she poured the wine in our glasses and gave us a second helping of pasta.

While the litigation was in session, Uncle Nano, Aunt Claretta, and Mama and Papa barely spoke to each other on the street. When we met Aunt Claretta, Papa muttered, his head bent, eyes on the cobblestones as he kept on walking, "Hi, Claretta."

"Go and kiss your Aunt, *bambini,*" he urged us.

"Family is important. It's the most important thing," he told us when we came back from kissing her.

After Papa and Uncle's partnership ended, Gabri, Antonio and I got up every morning at five o'clock. Before we went to school, we helped Papa assemble the mirrors he prepared for us the night before, and while we worked he told us many stories.

One morning Papa said, "*Bambini*, did I ever tell you about the time when your Mama and I were first married during World War II, and the Fascists decreed that every available man in Murano must go and march up and down the *fondamenta*?"

"Tell us Papa. Come on, tell us!"

Papa had his own opinion of the war, of Fascist's tactics, of their decrees and regulations, and did not go to march. He just plain did not want to march up and down the streets like a "clown." Or in and out of the outside cloisters of the Church of *San Pietro Martire* because it was a sacred place. Nor into the *Fondamenta dei Vetrai*, up and down, up and down. He did not want to listen to the echo of the Fascist sergeant's command who urged middle aged men to march erect in a straight line, to tap their feet in unison, to turn their head right and then left.

"I told your mama it was a matter of principle. Imagine, a grown man going to march under the church cloister," he said. "But your mama was preoccupied. She warned me many times that something would happen if I didn't go to march."

"Did you ever go, Papa," we asked.

"Never. No. Never. But your Mama was right, something did happen."

Papa paused to let us digest what he had said.

"One morning the Fascist Movement plastered big posters all over Murano."

Papa took a deep breath as our eyes, fixed on his face, searched for a clue.

"*Si, si*. All over Murano they plastered announcements that read, 'Whoever gives work to Nicolò Marchini will be severely punished'"

Papa said that Mama cried at home, hiding behind the kitchen curtains, afraid to go out, half admiring his convictions, half wondering what kind of a man she had married: a man who jeopardized his life because he was not willing to march up and down the streets in solidarity.

"You know, things happen for a reason. There is always a reason. Yes, there is," Papa pondered aloud.

"How did you and mama eat," Gabri asked.

"Two days after the announcement, my second cousin came, winked at me and said, 'Nico do you have time to engrave some vases for me?'"

Papa smiled and said, "He was the first. My friends all came to give me work. We did not starve. We got by like everyone else. Yes, we got by."

While the litigation about the split of the partnership was taking place, spring passed, and when summer came, Mama, Gelmina, my youngest siblings, and I went to Uncle Paolo's Villa in the mountain. Papa, Gabri, and Antonio stayed home and worked.

Late one Friday evening, we all went in the small town square, the one with the fountain with the red fishes in it and sat on one of the green benches waiting for Papa, Gabri and Antonio, who were arriving on the eight-thirty bus to spend the weekend with us.

We spied Silvana tagging after Papa, Gabri and Antonio, carrying her small suitcase, holding the traditional box of chocolates Aunt Claretta gave her to bring to us. She wore her smart summer outfit—that some day I would inherit—a light blue fisherman-style pants, a pale yellow sleeveless shirt tucked in, a multicolor cotton choker tied around her neck, white socks and tennis shoes, and her timid smile.

By the time our family returned from the mountains, in early September, the litigation was over, but it was still awkward to think that Mama, Papa, Aunt Claretta and Uncle Nano's relationship was not the same as before.

We children were not sure if Mama, Papa, and Uncle and Aunt Claretta were happy about the division of their goods as no one said anything about it.

How surprised my siblings and I were, when at the beginning of October, Mama set the table, using one of the white linen tablecloths she had made for her dowry. She added the napkins with her initials embroidered in one corner, her best china, and the crystal green glasses Papa had engraved for her. She used the silverware she inherited from her grandmother, and for a centerpiece the unique flower-vase her grandfather Giuseppe had designed and manufactured. She set an elegant table with the pride of a person who knows she came from a fine family, one who has a real sense of who she is, and knows that her roots are intertwined between the cobblestones, and embedded in the muddy, sandy bottom of the lagoon. And with each passing year, like the houses and palaces of Venice, sinks deeper and deeper into a proud permanence.

Mama stood by the table, in her finest attire, a green dress Aunt Susi had made for her, looking so beautiful in her quiet countenance. She had a natural lustrous milky skin, ebony hair which she expertly fixed up, and dark expressive eyes in which one could read many things. Eyes that told us Mama was worried.

When we came home from school, the table was set for thirteen, all of Mama and Papa's best friends, my godparents, who for years entertained each other, taking turns to host their gatherings. Mama focused her gaze on the big, red apple she was shining, and when Gabri said, "thirteen," with a questioning inflection in her voice, Mama told us that Uncle Nano and Aunt Claretta were also coming to dinner. She explained, pacing her words to control her voice, that the night before, Amelia, the oldest member of the *compagnia,* had called to say that Uncle Nano and Aunt Claretta would have liked to come as usual, and if it would be fine with Mama and Papa.

"Yes," Mama had said without hesitation. But we could read in her gestures, and in her movements, that she was nervous at the anticipation of that first encounter. She was concerned about what she would do when they first came in, and nervous at what Uncle and Aunt would say.

I turned my eyes in Papa's direction. Absorbed in his reveries, he helped Mama with the last touches. He opened the *frizzantino* wine, saved especially for the occasion as he sang *Santa Lucia* in his tenor voice, playing with the notes, prolonging the word "Luci-i-ia" when he came to it.

Papa began pestering Mama with unnecessary questions.

"Teresa, how is it going? Did you put the ducks in the oven? What about the potatoes? Yes, everything is fine. *Tutto bene, tutto a posto. Sì, Tutto a posto."* He was nervous, too, but a different kind of nervousness than Mama, one that calls for celebration, not worries. His nervousness encouraged others to relax and know that if the heart is in the right place, things will work out in the end.

At eight p.m., the doorbell rang. Outside, a loud voice rose, subsided, only to begin again. Then a buzz, an indistinct sound filled the atrium, as if a throng of people were approaching the door. We heard footsteps coming closer and closer.

Mama and Papa neared the door. My siblings and I positioned ourselves between the kitchen and the entrance hall so that we could say hello to all of the guests before we left for the evening to Great Aunt Nice's house where she would tell us Old Testament Bible stories: David in the Lion's Den, Samson and Delila, and Joseph and his Dreams.

One knock. An utterance. A pause.

Mama opened the door.

Uncle Nano and Aunt Claretta extended their hands to Mama and Papa, and they kissed each other on both cheeks.

We all watched: Amelia and her husband from the entrance hall, we children and Gelmina from within.

"Aunt Claretta," Mama said.

"Teresa."

We could read no reticence in the enunciation of those two names. No apologies, no useless explanations, only the sensible sound of a name that could mean so many things.

A few months after the October gathering, around one o'clock when I returned from school, Mama, Papa, Gelmina and my siblings were seated at the table.

"Nano has a lot of guts to ask you to testify," I heard Mama's voice saying. "I can't believe he wants you to testify against Remigio."

I walked over to kiss Mama, Papa, and Gelmina, then my siblings while Mama kept asking Papa if he were going to testify even if she knew the answer, even if we already knew what Papa would say in answer to her probing questions.

But Papa did not say what everyone expected him to utter. He did not repeat himself by reminding everyone one more time that after all Aunt Claretta and Uncle Nano were family, and family came first. No. This time he said, with the flare of a man who knows he is going to teach a new lesson to his children, "Teresa, I'm going to go and testify because what is right is right."

"What is right is right," he said looking at Mama.

As he finished his sentence, his chin moved downward in a decisive jolt to let everyone know that the discussion was over before it even started.

I sat at my usual place next to Margherita and Pietro where a warm bowl of pasta and peas awaited me. We children kept silent as we continued eating our pasta, while Gelmina said in a soft whisper, "Listen to your Papa. *Eh si,* how fortunate you are to have such a wonderful Papa."

I often think of what Aunt Claretta said about our Papa and of all of the extemporaneous memories he depicted in the form of flowers, and of the dark sky seasoned with his dreams in the shape of dazzling little stars. Like Van Gogh, he nurtured a tremendous passion for art. He did not paint *Starry Night*—a painting he admired—as Van Gogh did, and his name did not become famous. But unlike Van Gogh, he made sure the canvas of his life was layered with vibrant hues.

Now, in my family room, the painting Papa made during the litigation with Uncle Nano hangs on a special place on the wall. As I described before, a transparent vase with a bouquet of red and orange flowers sits with resolute flare on a dark brown surface. All around the flowers, a mixture of green-gray specks folds into uneven strokes of muted yellows that explode into vibrant hues of oranges in the background. Strange, when I look at the painting, I see my Papa's life in it: The background, a mixture of exploding emotions, contours a perfect symmetrical design in the center.

From Papa, I learned the importance of including in my own canvas a foreground and background filled with memories and dreams so that my memories may give me balance during the dark moments in my life, and through my dreams I may explore the firmament, a place filled with surprises and wonders.

Epilogue

My visit to Murano is almost over. In two days, I'll return to California. Gelmina has just come back from the Dolomite Mountains to attend to Mama. The humidity is high, and the heat of the August sun, unbearable. I wish Mama would let me turn on the air conditioner, but she does not like the cold air. So we sit, unable to move, with damp garments from the sweaty rivulets that continue to flow from our heads and bodies. We cannot breathe in the hundred percent humidity. I make sure the windows are all wide open, and the Venetian blinds up so we can still stare at the terracotta tile rooftops, at the church tower, at the pigeons perching on the windowsills of the church scanning the surroundings with tedious determination, looking for a grain here, a twig there, ready to hurl at their target.

Mama, Gelmina and I have just finished lunch, but the leftover food is still on the table. The doorbell rings, and Gelmina reminds me not to open the door without first looking outside the window to make sure it is not an immigrant selling socks. I lean my head out, and to my great pleasure I spy Tina looking up at the window, ready to wave.

"Tina," I shout. I run to open the door, a surge of life veiling my spirit, and jump two steps at a time down the stairs. We both begin to talk at the same time: I from the top of the stairs, and Tina from the entrance door.

I see that her face is gaunt, but her girlish figure, her lush, shining red hair, her smile, her affable mannerism is still with her. We embrace. I stand back to look into her eyes that say so much about her soul. I see the hurt she keeps away from sight, locked within her heart like a treasure she can reach no more, like a coffin buried deep within the earth.

"How are you," I ask.

When I compliment her on her slim figure, she tells me how many plain salads she had to eat to regain her normal weight. She reminds me of how fat she was when we saw each other last, and assures me that she is feeling much better. Her mouth utters a thousand words a minute, and I know that she is nervous.

We walk into the kitchen. Tina bends down to kiss Mama and Gelmina. Led by Gelmina, who has set a dish of pasta and has poured a glass of wine for her, Tina sits at the head of the table.

I ask her all kinds of questions about her family and our old friends.

Mama listens as she fans her face with the page of the newspaper, and Gelmina wipes her sweaty face with a white handkerchief, and utters from time to time, "*Mamma mia, che caldo, ragazze.*" Gelmina gets up and glances out of the window, searching for approaching clouds, hoping for the heat to subside soon.

The workers from the nearby factory are hammering on huge wooden boxes while shouting orders at each other. Murmurs from occasional passersby reach our ears, and an occasional bee looking for pollen flies in haste by the kitchen window. The radio from the next door neighbor is playing sixties music.

"Listen to this song," Tina says as she taps her foot on the terrazzo.

"It reminds me of when you went dancing every Sunday over at your friends' houses. You two went even during Lent, didn't you?" Gelmina teases us.

We laugh. Gelmina feels victorious for remembering our secrets.

"I need to go," Tina says after a while.

I glance at the clock and say, "Tina, I would like to go to the cemetery to say good bye to my father. Do you want to come?"

"*Si*," she says without hesitation. "I want to go, too."

I get ready while Gelmina gives Tina the third degree and my Mama listens in silence.

We walk through the *fondamenta* crowded with tourists. Some are looking for a shady place to rest. Some are fanning themselves, sitting on the bridge, eating ice cream and drinking water from plastic bottles. Arm in arm, just as if we were the same two girls of long ago, we cross the *Ponte*

Lungo, make a left, stop for a few minutes to inspect the empty front yard of the *Asilo Infantile* that is now a wide open area with no oleander partitions.

I chuckle as I chant, *"Fie e fioi fa pecà, fioi e fie fa pecà,"* and Tina joins me. We talk about the nuns who are not there anymore, and of Sister Agata's iron hand. We remind each other of all the little pebbles we ingested when we were little girls, and of how much fun we had growing up.

At the arch in *Fondamenta Degli Angeli*, we turn and proceed on the paved pathway that is now lined on each side by apartment buildings. Tina becomes silent, and as I do not want to disturb her thoughts, I wave to the few older ladies who stare at us as if they wanted to say something, but do not.

We enter the cemetery gate. I turn my head around to admire all of the flowers and the tall proud cypresses. I listen to the birds chirping and flapping their wings as they move from tree to tree, and the old familiar, peaceful feeling engulfs me. I turn towards Tina. She bends down, pulls a weed by the white, marble cross on one of the tombs. With the same resolute steps I've seen her take many times before, she walks to the next one, and to the one a little further down that same aisle. She stoops over on the headstone while I stand and watch this energetic woman gently kissing the face in the picture.

"These are my three men," she tells me. "My father, my husband and my brother."

She pauses a moment to steady her voice, then as if to herself she continues, "Look, they all died so young, so full of life."

With the tips of her fingers, she caresses her brother's face on the picture. "I nursed my brother till the end. He only wanted me to take care of him."

I want to say something but am unable to utter a single syllable.

Tina comes near me, pulls me by the hand and says, "Where is your father?"

The sound of small pebbles crunching under our sandals, and the voices of two ladies talking to each other by the fountain, echo throughout. We walk to the end of a dirt path, and stop to pray by Papa's tomb. His picture has faded, but the expression in his face still reflects the same enthusiasm and reverence he nurtured for life.

"My papa!" I mull over this sweet word in my mind and wish he were still with us, cheering us on, dreaming his impossible dreams, helping us to construct our memories, one small celebration at a time. I wish he were still here to reassure us with his magic tricks, with his fantastic stories, with his small lessons of love. I wish I could hear the sound of his voice one more time telling us that a united family is the synthesis of the most melodic and harmonious notes of life.

But he is gone forever.

Once outside the cemetery, Tina and I sit on the steps, not really saying much, both engaged in our own thoughts and memories.

"I'd like you to come over tonight," Tina says as she gets up, "to visit with me and my mother for awhile."

At nine o'clock that evening, when I enter Tina's kitchen, I notice lots of pictures spread on the wooden table's shiny surface. Tina's mother is holding a small, black and white one. When she sees me, she comes forward, and with open arms she embraces me.

"*Bambina*, look at this picture. How beautiful you both were," she says as she chuckles, her eyes on the two young girls standing in front of her credenza.

Beautiful is an affectionate adjective, one which does not fit the picture because when I see it, I laugh at our expressions. I'm amused by our old fashioned attire, our skinny legs, Tina's wide smile, and my curly hair. One by one, we look at all the pictures, and stare at fragments of our past on Tina's kitchen table. We talk about our siblings, our friends, Sele, Davide, Aldo, Renzo, and all the wonderful times we had growing up in Murano. We reminisce about that part of our lives that we hold within, like the most precious treasure.

When I say goodnight to Tina's mother, Tina walks with me through the deserted *fondamenta*.

The *fondamenta* of my native island of Murano are silent, breathless by the ancient beauty of its surrounding. I only hear the sound of Tina's and my sandals tapping on the cobblestones. I stop at the foot of the bridge to imbue myself with the magic of the evening: the houses with their shuttered windows and the flickering lights reflecting on the long mirror of glassy green water.

I pause. I do not want to miss this moment. A faint perception of reality: A mystical world in which fantasy and reality fuse into one. I savor the beauty of it all, just like I savor the stories of my childhood veiled by time, that have become more magical with each passing year.

Dong. . .Dong. . .Dong. . .The ancient tower—ancient as people's morals and traditions—with its round, grayish, dimly lit face, strikes once more. The tower is still keeping a watchful eye on the island and its inhabitants.

Her "Dongs" seem to say, "Sing with me," and I accept the invitation and start counting, "One, two, three. . . twelve," the way I used to as a child.

Tina and I sit together on the bridge we have crossed a thousand times before, the same bridge I crossed with my siblings and my best friends to go to school, to church, to the bakery. The bridge I convened with my friends to exchange secrets. The steps where I sat, chin on my knees, waiting for Tina after school so we could walk together, stop by the church grounds to swing, to talk, to take the long way home while our mothers waited in vain to serve us lunch, table set, pot on the stove ready to go.

We sit in silence, and I am glad to share this moment. I wonder how many stories have passed along this same path. I wonder how much sorrow and joy one can read into it.

"It's so beautiful. Isn't it beautiful?" I say, almost to myself.

"You miss Murano, don't you," Tina says.

It's a question I have asked myself a hundred times while living in the United States. I do not need to think about my answer.

"There is always something to miss. I miss my family and friends," I say with conviction.

I want to say more, but I do not. I stand up. We start walking. A timid hum rises from my throat and politely dances through the street. A soft reassuring sound, one which I do not want this old ancient island, and its inhabitants to hear. It is the tune of my favorite song, whose words I have kept in my wallet for many years, and that fully answer Tina's question. A song that tells of spacious skies, mountains high, amber waves of grain.

A song not embedded in the ancient cobblestones, but within my heart.

Favorite Family Recipes

ZALETI

Grandfather's Polenta Cookies, a typical Muranese old fashioned dessert

⅔ cup	yellow polenta (cornmeal)
1½ cups	flour
⅓ cup	sugar
8 tablespoons	butter, softened
3 large	egg yolks
⅓ cup	pine nuts
½ cup	seedless white raisins
½ cup	* cedrini (orange peel) or a grated rind of one lemon
¼ teaspoon	salt
½ teaspoon	vanilla extract
½ teaspoon	rum extract

Pour the polenta and the flour into a large bowl and mix them together. Work in the soft butter. Beat the egg yolks and the sugar by hand, and pour into mixture. Add the rest of the ingredients and knead the mixture into an even consistency.

Shape each individual cookie into a medium sized ball. Flatten it into an oval shape.

Bake in a preheated 325 oven for 20 minutes or until cookies are light golden brown.

*CEDRINI

Cut the rind of a large orange in long narrow strips and soak them overnight in water.

Drain and boil the strips with ⅓ cup of sugar for approximately 10 minutes over medium heat (no water added).

Place ¼ cup of granulated sugar on a dinner plate, then roll the cooked orange rind on the plate and let it cool off for half an hour. Cut the strips into small cubes.

CREMA DI ZABAIONE

Aunt Nice made this traditional Italian dessert for everyone during Christening, First Communion and Confirmation celebrations.

12	egg yolks
¾ cup	granulated sugar
1 ½ cups	sweet Marsala wine

Whisk eggs and sugar for a few minutes in a double boiler. Add the Marsala wine and continue to whisk till the mixture is nice and thick. Place Zabaione into small dessert dishes or glasses and serve hot. Or put dessert dishes in refrigerator and eat cold. Our family always ate it hot.

Serves 8-10

MEAT SAUCE

Grandfather and Aunt Claretta's Meat Sauce

1 pound	ground meat
½ small	onion, finely chopped
2 baby	carrots, finely chopped
1 stalk	celery, finely chopped
12 needles	fresh rosemary
4 whole	cloves
4 tablespoons	olive oil
2 tablespoons	butter
½ cup	red wine
2 cubes	beef bouillon
2 cans	29 oz. tomato sauce
½ cup	water

Sauté onion, celery, carrots, cloves and rosemary in oil, approximately five minutes. Add the meat, butter, red wine, bouillon cubes and cook until the wine has evaporated and the meat is brown. Pour in the two cans of tomato sauce and the ½ cup of water. Bring to a boil, then cover the pan and lower the heat. Cook slowly for 3½ hours, or until the sauce is dark red and the oil on the surface is translucent. Mix occasionally to make sure that the sauce does not stick to the bottom of the pan.

Delicious with any kind of pasta.
Serve with grated Parmesan cheese.
You may double the recipe and freeze the remainder of the sauce.

INSALATA RUSSA

My sister-in-law, Rosanna, gave me this recipe many years ago. It's delicious and quick to prepare.

2 ⅓	pounds	potatoes
10	eggs	hard boiled, chopped
1	cup	mayonnaise
2	cups	Italian Mix Giardiniera
2	teaspoons	salt
2	teaspoons	lemon pepper

Peal, cut, and boil the potatoes till tender. Do not overcook.
Drain and grind the Giardiniera.
Let the potatoes cool, then add the rest of the ingredients. Mix to a creamy consistency. Mold the mixture in an elegant serving dish, place a thin layer of mayonnaise on top and decorate with colorful raw vegetables. Great for parties, picnics, or just as an added tasteful dish with meat, or fish.

It can be served with salad before the meal. Place lettuce on dish. Add an ice cream scoop of Insalata Russa in the center. Garnish with a couple of black olives, and a thin slice of rolled-up prosciutto, and serve.

Insalata Russa can be made in many different ways. Mother made Insalata Russa with potatoes, boiled fresh vegetables such as peas and carrots and pickled capers. At times she added either canned tuna or fresh boiled fish to the mixture.

PEPERONATA

Mama Teresa's Peperonata

3	large	red and yellow sweet pepper
1	large	eggplant
1	large	clove of garlic, finely chopped
1	large	onion
1	large	tomato
2	medium	zucchini
⅓	cup	olive oil
1		bouillon cube, or salt to taste

Cut all of the vegetables in small cubes. Discard some of the excess white pulp in the eggplant (leave only 1" from outer layer). Also discard the sweet pepper's seeds.

Sauté garlic and onion in olive oil till golden brown. Add the rest of the ingredients, the bouillon cube or the salt, whichever you prefer. Place lid on sauce pan, and let it simmer. Stir occasionally. The Peperonata is ready when the water from the vapor has disappeared, and the oil is translucent.

Serves 6.

There are different ways of preparing peperonata. Some people omit the zucchini, some make it only with red and yellow peppers. My mother used all of the above ingredients, and that is the way I like it best. It's great with any kind of meat or poultry. It's delicious even spread on bread, or as an extra delicacy for a light luncheon. You may serve it hot or cold.

If you wish to make it only with red and yellow sweet peppers (5 or 6), then sauté garlic and onion in olive oil to a golden brown. Add the sweet peppers and ½ bouillon cube or salt to taste, and cook till they are tender and the oil is translucent (approximately 30 to 40 minutes). Italians cook their vegetables much longer then we do here in the United States.

I use the Knorr bouillon cube to flavor my food because I think that it adds a special flavor to the food. I've tried different ones, but the flavors are not the same.

RISOTTO WITH CLAMS OR MUSSELS
Mama Teresa's Risotto

2	tablespoons	butter
¼	cup + 2 Tbsp.	olive oil
6	cups	liquid (water and fish stock)
½	glass	dry white wine
2	medium	cloves of garlic, finely chopped
2	tablespoons	lemon juice, fresh
2	tablespoons	parsley, minced
2	tablespoons	grated Parmesan cheese
1⅓	cups	Italian rice
2	pounds	clams or mussels or both salt to taste
½	cup	water

Scrub and rinse the clams or mussels thoroughly.

In a saucepan, heat the ½cup of water, the 2 Tbsp. of olive oil, one squeeze of lemon, one clove of garlic and a pinch of salt. Bring to boil. Pour in the clams or mussels and cover tightly until they open. Shell and place them in a separate container, but save the liquid.

In a different pan, heat oil, garlic, and gently sauté till the garlic is light golden brown. Add the wine and three cups of liquid and bring to a boil.

Pour 1⅓ cups of Italian rice into pan and mix with a wooden spoon. Cook slowly over medium to low heat so that the rice does not stick to the bottom of the pan. Add liquid as needed, mixing the rice for approximately 20 to 25 minutes or till tender. Before the risotto is completely cooked, taste to see if salt is needed. Three minutes before the rice is ready, add the butter, the fish, the lemon, the Parmesan cheese and the parsley. Mix to a creamy paste.

The finished risotto should be creamy, not watery, and of course delicious. Pour risotto directly into serving dishes.

Serve hot at once. Italians eat risotto as a first dish before they serve the main course.

Serves approximately 4 to 6.

If you use the dish as a main course, double the recipe.
You may use the same recipe to make risotto with prawns.

To Order More:

You may order directly from Falcone Books by writing to our Email address or P.O. Box:

Email Address: orders@falconebooks.com
or
Fill out form and send with check to:
Falcone Books
P.O. Box 3463
Walnut Creek, CA 94598

Name:
Address:
City: State: Zip:
Phone: (   )
Each book $ 16.95+ CA sales tax 8.25% only when ordering through Falcone Books.
Free shipping and handling on retail sales within the Continental US with P.O. Box Order, or orders@falconebooks.com

----

Order online at:
http://www.falconebooks.com
http://www.trafford.com/05-1443
http://www.amazon.com

We also encourage you to patronize your local bookstore. Most stores will order any title that they do not stock.

A window onto Italian Culture...